# WORLD BAYONETS
## 1800 TO THE PRESENT

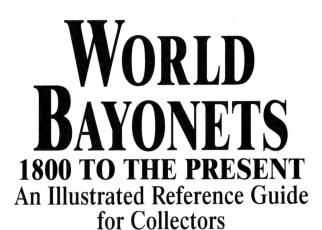

# WORLD BAYONETS

## 1800 TO THE PRESENT
### An Illustrated Reference Guide
### for Collectors

## ANTHONY CARTER

ARMS AND
ARMOUR

This edition published in 1996.
First published in Great Britain in 1984 by
**Arms and Armour Press**
An Imprint of the Cassell Group
Wellington House, 125 Strand, London WC2R 0BB

Distributed in the USA by Sterling Publishing Co. Inc.,
387 Park Avenue South, New York, NY 10016-8810.

Reprinted 1997

British Library Cataloguing-in-Publication Data:
a catalogue record for this book is available from the British Library

ISBN 1-85409-344-4

Designed and edited by DAG Publications Ltd.
Designed by David Gibbons; printed and bound in Great Britain.

**Acknowledgements**
I must thank Harold Preston and J. and B. Hoath for kindly
allowing me to photograph selected items from their collections.
In order to revise the values as accurately as possible for this fourth
edition I sought the advice of three well-known collectors, Brian
Malis, John Oliver and Roy Williams, and I am most grateful for
their cooperation. Graham Priest gave me advice, and Roger Evans
kindly sent me information about the origin of the plug bayonet
and lent photographs of examples in his own collection.
John Oliver also lent me the modern bayonets to photograph,
and Roy Williams took the jacket photograph.

# CONTENTS

**Introduction**
The History of the Bayonet, 6
Collecting Bayonets, 14
Cleaning and Restoration, 15
Blades, 16
Hilts, 17
Scabbards and Belt Frogs, 19
Displaying a Collection, 21

**Bibliography, 23**

**Price Guide for 1996/7, 25**

**The Plates** *(plate numbers)*

# INTRODUCTION

## The History of the Bayonet

The history and development of the bayonet from 1570 to the present covers four major changes in design. The earliest dagger-shaped plug bayonets which fitted into the muskets' barrels were replaced by slim-bladed socket bayonets which clipped over the barrels. These were gradually phased out in preference for sword bayonets which became lighter and shorter until the modern knife bayonets were almost universally adopted. If the bayonet had been allowed to develop in its purest form as a secondary weapon to the musket or rifle, its history would be comparatively simple. However, the arms designers frequently tried to combine the bayonet with another weapon or tool. Initially this intention made sense when an infantryman carried both a bayonet and a shortsword which could be combined in a single sword bayonet. In the ensuing years bayonets were combined with swords, sabres, cutlasses, saws, lances, trowels, machetes, wire-cutters, bowie knives, daggers and trench knives. After nearly four hundred years of trial and development one would assume that by the end of the twentieth century an ideal bayonet would have been found, but the search for a better weapon still goes on, and to this day there is no universally approved type in service.

It is now accepted that the bayonet originated in the Basque region of northern Spain in the late sixteenth century, 1570–80. During the same period the cutlers in Bayonne in southern France, also in the Basque region, were producing a regional form of dagger called a *bayonnette*. By the 1640s the hilts of these daggers were being altered to fit within the muzzles of firearms, and their local name remained with them as their use spread abroad.

The plug bayonet evolved from the Spanish boar spear which had a broad double-edged blade and a straight crossguard. Boar hunting was a particularly popular sport amongst the Spanish nobility and landed gentry. The wild boar is extremely dangerous when wounded, and a nobleman armed with a muzzle-loading musket was accompanied by huntsmen and footmen armed with long boar spears. A spear head, possibly with part of a broken shaft attached, must have been modified by tapering the wood to fit within the muzzle. This simple concept gave the marksman a defence against a wounded animal. The straight crossguard was retained to prevent too much penetration, and the next step was to reshape the hilt with a rounded bulbous section which doubled as a barrel stop and gave a much improved hand grip. The use of this sporting plug bayonet spread across Europe through France to Germany and Italy, although it took several decades before it was adopted for military use.

The most important development in the use of military tactics was taking place in northern Europe where King Gustavus Adolphus of Sweden (1611–32) introduced conscription, and raised an army which for the first time was paid, fed and equipped by the state. His well-organised infantry fought the Danes, Russians and Poles, and although the king died in battle, the success of Swedish troops during the Thirty Years War (1615–48) ensured that all Europe studied their organisation and tactics. At that time the infantry contained both musketeers and pikemen. The musketeers discharged their cumbersome firearms in a volley,

**Plug Bayonets,** left to right: English Board of Ordnance Pattern c.1690, oak grip, brass pommel and crossguard, R7/8, £500-700; English Officer's bayonet c.1690, ivory grip with silver piqué work, silver mounts on hilt and scab- bard, R10, £2,000+. R.D.C. Evans collection

but then required protection while they reloaded, a process which could take as long as two minutes. The pikemen, often in three ranks, presented the enemy with an almost inpenetrable fence of spikes. These tactics meant that a large pro-

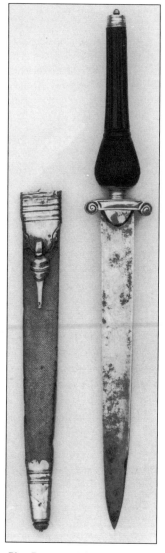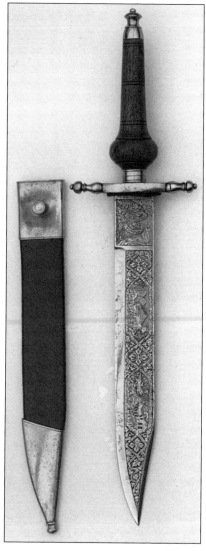

**Plug Bayonets**, left to right: French Louis XV plug bayonet with reversible hilt, ebony grip, silver mounts on the hilt and shagreen scabbard, R10, £2,000+; Spanish Toledo made hunting bayonet c.1880, fruit wood grip, steel mounts and good quality etched blade, R7, about £250. R.D.C. Evans collection

portion of any infantry force consisted of pikemen whose task was entirely defensive. If those men could be employed as musketeers, the number of offensive troops would be almost doubled. The plug bayonet made this possible by allowing the musketeers to protect themselves, although the drawback was that reloading or firing could not be performed with a plug bayonet in the muzzle.

It took nearly a century for the plug bayonet to evolve from a hunting weapon to a widely accepted infantry arm. Contemporary English records first mention them in 1662, and they were being issued to troops within a decade. It soon became apparent that the problem with reloading was a serious drawback, and a new type of bayonet was needed, one which allowed the troops to fire and reload with fixed bayonets. The socket bayonet with a blade attached to a tube or socket which fitted over the barrel provided the answer. The plug bayonet was obsolete throughout Europe within a few years, but in Spain it continued in use purely as a sporting arm for another two hundred years; beautifully made examples were made as late as the 1890s.

By 1720 new, lighter flintlock muskets were being introduced; the French Model 1717 Charleville musket and the British Long Pattern musket – the Brown Bess. Infantry tactics of the period required the troops to stand steady and return fire whether in line, three deep, or in defensive formed squares. The handier lighter muskets were better for bayonet fighting, but in practice the troops rarely closed. Volley after volley would be exchanged until one side broke ranks and either fled or retreated. The victors, seeing their opponents waver, would then advance with fixed bayonets. Their threat alone usually carried the day. In defence against cavalry charges, infantry squares bristling with bayonets were virtually impregnable. The spirit of the pike lived on, and for that reason the blades evolved into straight thrusting weapons with little or no cutting edges. The slim triangular blade proved ideal and was almost universally adopted.

The earliest socket bayonets had a simple L-shaped slot which allowed the bayonet to pass over the foresight; then, twisting the socket to the side loosely locked the bayonet in position against the sight. An improvement was made by cutting an extra leg to form a zig-zag slot. This method of attachment was in use by 1720 (**192**). Thereafter, most improvements were made to the method of attachment, springs were attached to the sides of the sockets to lock the bayonets in position, others were held in place by springs on the musket which clipped over a lip on the socket. By the mid-nineteenth century the locking ring placed in the middle of the socket was in widespread use. The ring was shaped with a bridge which allowed the foresight to pass through the ring; it was then locked in place by twisting the ring (**205**, **216**, **226**, **241–2**). The many minor changes made to the British socket bayonet are illustrated and described in Graham Priest's *The Brown Bess Bayonet 1720–1860*.

The triangular blade was not universally adopted. The Austrians preferred a cruciform shape as did the French on their M 1866 for the Gendarmerie (**49**), the Turks on their M 1874 (**181**) and the Russians on their Berdan and M 1891 (**253**). A few heavy sword socket bayonets were introduced for specialist troops, particularly in Austria and Britain (**196**, **202** and **203**), but these clumsy designs were eventually replaced by sword bayonets with conventional hilts.

9

The socket bayonet lasted in service for two and a half centuries before being completely replaced by the modern knife bayonet. If the British No. 4 spike bayonet is included, then in the Second World War two of the major combatants, the Russians and British, fought mainly with sockets.

During the First World War socket bayonets, which had been declared obsolete in the nineteenth century, sold as government surplus, and then stored in the warehouses of private arms dealers in Belgium and Germany, were requisitioned by the Germans. These old bayonets originally from Austria, Belgium, Britain, France and the United States had the sockets removed and were fitted with new steel or brass hilts, and were put into service once more (**123–5**).

It was not until the 1860s that the sword bayonet became the infantryman's weapon. Most foot soldiers had previously been equipped with a smooth-bore flintlock musket, a socket bayonet and a shortsword or hanger. By the late eighteenth century, sword bayonets began to appear in the hands of élite troops equipped with rifled firearms. In the German states Jaegers – hunters and gamekeepers armed with rifles – formed units of marksmen, and by 1800 Britain had raised a corps equipped with dark green uniforms, Baker rifles and sword bayonets who acted as light infantry and formed the skirmish line in battle. The sword bayonets had a broad single-edged blade, a brass hilt and a D-shaped knuckleguard (**193**). Their design was based on the German *Hirschfänger*, a hunting shortsword traditionally worn by Jaegers. When Brunswick rifles were introduced in the 1830s a new sword bayonet was adopted with a broader double-edged blade, a symmetrical brass hilt and straight crossguard (**198** and **204**). The Brunswick design owed much to the French infantry shortsword introduced in 1831 which in turn was based on the ancient Roman *gladius*.

Sword bayonets remained an élite arm until the late 1860s. The British widened their issue to include the artillery, but the infantry continued to carry socket bayonets, and in most armies a separate shortsword.

In France a revolutionary change in bayonet blade design was made which influenced the shape of bayonets throughout the world for the next fifty years. Their brass-hilted Model 1840 sabre bayonet (**45**) had been introduced with a recurving blade based on the Indo-Persian *yataghan*, a weapon which had spread to Turkey and the Balkans. The yataghan blade provided a curved cutting edge and a thrusting point in line with the barrel. Initially this bayonet and its derivatives, the Models 1842 and 1842/59 (**46–7**), were only issued to élite troops. Britain issued a copy of the M 1842 with a ribbed brass hilt to the artillery in 1852 (**206**), but by 1856 had adoped yataghan-bladed bayonets with steel hilts and chequered black leather grips (**209**). However, in 1866 the French decided to issue their new Chassepot rifle and M 1866 sabre bayonet not just to élite troops but to all their infantry. Most of Europe followed with remarkable speed. The Belgians adopted a virtual copy of the French bayonet in 1868 as did the Bavarians in 1869 (**68**) and the Dutch in 1873 (**137**). The Austrians (**5–6**) and Danes (**42**) introduced their M 1867 yataghan bayonets a year after the French, but in both cases with steel hilts and chequered leather grips similar to the British.

The yataghan sword bayonet became the accepted design for an infantry bayonet, but there were exceptions. The Italians adopted a straight single-edged blade in 1870 (**147–8**), and the Prussians, having defeated France in the war of 1870–1 and having no wish to copy anything French, also introduced a similar straight single-edged blade in 1871 (**69**). At the same time the fashion for issuing different blade forms to different units continued, and for a brief period the pipeback blade with a single cutting edge and broader double-edged point was adopted by the British Sappers and Miners in 1855 (**207**), the Prussian Fusiliers in 1860 (**65**) and in slightly different form by the Prussian Jaegers in 1865 (**66**). A much slimmer version of the pipeback blade was eventually adopted as the standard German infantry bayonet in 1898 (**86, 88**) and by the Turks in 1903 (**187**).

Still more sword bayonets were introduced for branches of the armed forces other than the infantry. Most designs attempted to combine the bayonet with another weapon or tool. Britain issued heavy cutlass bayonets to the Royal Navy in 1859 (**210–11**) and 1871 (**214**), and saw-backed sword bayonets to the artillery in 1875 (**215**) and 1879 (**217**). In 1870 Lord Elcho, Earl of Wemyss, designed a saw-backed bayonet with a broad spear point (**213**) which, although issued for trials, was not adopted. Elsewhere saw-backed bayonets were issued to the Belgian Pioneers in 1868 (**22**) and the Prussian Pioneers in 1865 (**67**). The Bavarians followed suit in 1871 (**72**). In some cases, particularly in Germany, these new bayonets replaced both an obsolete socket bayonet and a saw-backed shortsword. In 1871 the Germans also introduced a new practice of issuing saw-backed versions of their infantry bayonet to six per cent of their troops, usually NCOs. Among other combination tool bayonets that were introduced, the American trowel bayonet of 1873 (**243**) was one of the most unusual, although only one of many types tried by the Americans; some of their trowel bayonets even had one edge saw-backed.

The last quarter of the nineteenth century witnessed more changes in the design of the bayonet. The French changed their M 1866 yataghan blade for the M 1874 (**50**) with a straight tapering T-backed blade intended solely for thrusting. Twelve years later in 1886 they adopted a completely new design with the Lebel rifle, and introduced a slim cruciform blade, 520mm (20.5in) long, again suitable only for thrusting (**52–6**). The Germans had recently adopted a more modern M 71/84 knife bayonet (**80–2**), but faced with the French advantage in reach they were forced to reconsider, and eventually adopted the long slim-bladed M 1898 as their principal infantry bayonet.

By 1900 there was still no consensus of opinion over the design of the ideal infantry bayonet. Some nations favoured the knife bayonet while others preferred the sword bayonets with their longer reach. If anything, design had diversified from country to country, although the next thirty years would see the gradual acceptance of the knife bayonet. In 1900 the Russian army was equipped with cruciform-bladed socket bayonets (**253**), the Austrians (**11–12**), Belgians (**28**) and Italians (**153**) with single-edged knife bayonets adopted in 1886–8, 1889 and 1891 respectively. The Germans had their long M 1898 and the French their cruciform-bladed épée bayonet, both of the same length. In just twenty-one years, from 1886 to 1907, the British changed from long to short blades then back to long ones. The P 1886 and 1887 sword bayonets (**218–20**) had 470mm (18.5in) long, single-edged blades, similar to the German M 1871.

11

Most were issued with Martini-Henry rifles and sent to India, because a year later in 1888 a new infantry bayonet was introduced with a shorter 305mm (12in) double-edged blade (**221–4**) for issue with the Lee-Metford, then the Lee-Enfield rifles. Britain retained the same blade on the P 1903 (**225**) for the Short Magazine Lee-Enfield, but in 1907 introduced a much longer 432mm (17in) single-edged blade (**228–9**). Two years earlier the Americans adopted their M 1905 Springfield bayonet with a 405mm (16in) blade (**245**) in preference to their much shorter M 1892 (**244**).

The First World War began with most of the opposing armies equipped for a war of movement, of cavalry charges and infantry battles fought with fixed sword bayonets where reach was thought important when two regiments clashed. The war soon developed into stalemate with the armies dug in behind rows of barbed wire. In the confined space of the trenches the widespread use of clubs and spades became common in hand-to-hand combat. Steel helmets were issued to all armies, and in some cases even body armour. Trench or combat knives were also carried by most combatants, and some German knives were made to fit on the rifles (**101–2**). The swept-forward quillons on crossguards were removed by the British and French (**229, 53**) in 1915 and thereafter their bayonets were produced without them. During the war the Germans introduced gradually shorter bayonets from 520mm (20.5in) to 368mm (14.5in), then to 300mm (11.8in) and finally to 250mm (9.84in), the length of their M 84/98 knife bayonet which eventually became their standard bayonet from 1920 until 1945.

No lessons had been learned from the First World War that were acceptable to all armies. The French began shortening some of their bayonets in 1935 (**35**). The British examined the reports from field hospitals and erroneously assumed that bayonets had hardly been used during the war because few soldiers had been admitted with bayonet wounds. The fact that bayonets were used to kill, not wound, was somehow missed completely. After trials in the 1930s the first of the No. 4 spike bayonet series was introduced with a short cruciform blade (**231–4**) whose design owed much to the old socket bayonets.

By 1939 the German troops were equipped with their short M 84/98, but the Russians retained their M 1891 and M 1891/30 cruciform socket bayonets. The Japanese still used their long M 1897 bayonets (**160–2**) and the Americans their M 1905, although these were shortened in 1942 to a length of 24.7cm (10in). The Italians kept their M 1891 bayonets, but introduced several very short knife bayonets for use on their sub-machine guns (**156–9**). They also used folding bayonets on some carbines, as did the Russians (**256**).

Two wartime bayonets adopted in Britain and the USA eventually proved the most influential on post-war design. In 1944 Britain introduced the No. 5 Carbine for use in jungle warfare where accuracy at long range was not a priority. The carbine had a flash-hider which prevented the use of the No. 4 spike bayonets, so a new No. 5 knife bayonet (**236**) was introduced with a short 191mm (7.5in) single-edged blade and a bowie point which doubled as a combat knife. The hilt had smooth wood grips and a large muzzle ring to fit over the flash-hider. Although adopted initially for use in the Burmese jungle, it influenced the design of most post-war British bayonets (**237–40**) which all utilised the same blade. Similar types were adopted in Canada (**36**), Australia, New Zealand and India. The original No. 5, although now with plastic grips, is still in use with the Sterling sub-machine gun.

The Americans had an excellent combat knife, the M3, adopted in 1943, which was strong, light and well balanced. Its 172mm (6.75in) blade was single-edged but the back was sharpened for the last 89mm (3.5in), giving it a double-edged point. The hilt, made of leather rings, was comfortable to hold. In 1944 the M3 knife was altered by fitting a new crossguard and pommel to become the M4 bayonet (**249**) for issue with the M1 Carbine, a light, handy weapon intended for troops previously armed with pistols. After the war the M4's short blade was adopted for the M5, M6 and M7 bayonets (**250–2**). The M4 was also issued in Italy and the Netherlands, and the M5 in Denmark. The blade alone was copied on bayonets issued by the Dutch, Germans, Norwegians and Swedes.

These simple knife bayonets would have been refined and improved if the Russians had not adopted a saw-backed, bowie-bladed, wire-cutting bayonet (**258**) with their post-war Kalashnikov rifles. Millions of these rifles have been exported throughout the world, and the designs of both rifle and bayonet have influenced development in the West. Both Britain and the United States adopted

Modern wire-cutting bayonets, left to right: East German AKM Bayonet, R3, down to £20; British SA 80 Bayonet, R5, £55-60; American M9, R6, £120+
John Oliver collection

13

similar multi-purpose bayonets in the mid-1980s. The American version, the M9, is well thought out and extremely well made. Other nations, particularly the Swiss, who also have an export market, seem to be concentrating on simple knife bayonets with double-edged blades and excellent hilts. Whether bayonet design will be dominated by the multi-purpose bayonet in the next century or will revert to much simpler forms is uncertain.

The bayonet will continue to be issued for the foreseeable future. The charge with fixed bayonets may be history, but it is still needed for riot control, guarding prisoners and house to house searches. Soldiers will always need knives, but it will be a failure of modern bayonet design if troops prefer to acquire their own combat knives when equipped with their service bayonets.

## Collecting Bayonets

The brief history of bayonets and the illustrations in this book will give the novice some idea of the enormous variety of bayonets available. Collecting began seriously in the 1960s, although a few collections were formed in the 1930s. A handful of books were published which helped identification, but information in any depth was hard to find. By the 1970s there were at least eight specialist dealers in the United Kingdom, most of whom published catalogues of their stock. Wholesale dealers purchased large quantities of surplus bayonets from foreign governments, and the specialists often went abroad to buy stock and private collections. The prices were ridiculously low in comparison to those of today, but not when inflation is taken into account. At that time cars and houses sold for about one-tenth of their present values.

Today most of the old warehouses have been cleared out, government stocks of obsolete arms have been sold, and there are far fewer old weapons of all kinds on the market. Prices have therefore soared, and the demand for the rarer items is very strong. Only a very few dealers still specialise in the subject, but most militaria and arms shops include a selection for sale.

The last decade has witnessed a tremendous increase in the number of books published on the subject, and most are listed in the Bibliography. Research has progressed from simply identifying a type to describing its minor variations, listing the known makers and explaining regimental markings. Consequently, bayonets that were once dismissed as too common to be worth more than a few pounds, like the French Model 1866 Sabre Bayonet, are now examined for rare makers' markings and the production dates in relation to the Franco-Prussian War of 1870-1 are taken into account. Similarly, a German Model 98/05 is checked to see if it was made by a rare maker, if it has any unit markings and, most importantly, to ascertain whether it is a Prussian, Bavarian or Saxon example. All these factors can affect its worth to collectors.

A few years ago, whether a bayonet had its original belt frog or not was of little interest, but now even these are collected. Most have been identified, and are often sold separately. Some collectors even try to find the original frog, belt and cartridge pouches to make up a set.

Where does one find bayonets now that most of the specialist dealers have retired? The auctioneers Wallis & Wallis, Weller & Dufty and Kent Sales include them in their regular sales, but some experience and knowledge of the market is required before attending a sale.

The greatest recent change to the whole field of militaria collecting is in the proliferation of Arms Fairs. A list of the 1996 fairs would show over one hundred and eighty being held throughout the country. Some are little more than collectors' gatherings with a few dealers attending, but others, such as those held in London, Bedford, Birmingham, Dunstable, Solihull and Nottingham, are large events, and well worth visiting. Fifty or a hundred dealers will have stands displaying their goods for sale. The fairs are usually well publicised, and their dates published in the collectors' magazines.

At the fairs most items are clearly priced, and they can be examined at leisure. You will have the opportunity to meet not only the dealers, but fellow collectors who are generally a friendly and knowledgeable bunch. Don't be afraid to haggle, but don't be aggressive, just ask politely for the best price on a particular item. Most dealers expect such questions and price their stock accordingly.

Find out where your nearest shop specialising in militaria is located, and make yourself and your interests known. Ask before you take something off the wall to examine it, and don't spend hours chattering about your hobby. Most dealers do have work to do apart from serving customers, and although they too are usually enthiusiasts, they are busy. Try to visit street markets, especially the Portobello Road in London on Saturdays. Furthermore, don't ignore your local antique shops. Many of the rarest bayonets have been discovered in shops that do not specialise in them.

Finally, don't be too afraid of fakes, although they do exist. This guide identifies certain types that have been reproduced, as distinct from being faked. Although some are well made, it should not take long to discover the difference. In fact, they have been manufactured, usually in India, not to deceive but to be sold as decorative reproductions for the North American market at prices well below the genuine article. Sadly, a few have been artificially aged and passed off as originals. Even an antique dealer without specialist knowledge may buy in a sword or bayonet without realising when it was made.

## Cleaning and Restoration

The first thing most collectors do after buying a new bayonet is to take it home and clean it. It is a perfectly natural desire to want to preserve an old weapon, and at the very least it will need wiping with an oily cloth to remove fingerprints before being put away or hung in a display. The problems arise when it requires more work. Perhaps there is rust on the blade or under the grips, the press stud may be sticking, the brass is dull or the leather dry and brittle. How far should restoration be taken and what tools should be used? There are no straightforward answers because neither dealers, museum staff nor even collectors can agree. The result of any cleaning must be to prevent further deterioration to the overall condition of the bayonet, and to preserve it for the future. The second and optimal result is to restore it as near as possible to its original condition, but the extent to which this work is considered desirable or in some cases even ethical is open to debate. The decision has to rest with the owner, for what may be perfectly acceptable to one collector may be anathema to another. I know one American collector who had an intense dislike of polished brass and insists that what many call tarnish or even dirt is in fact age patina and should be preserved. I have also met collectors who refuse even to clean their bayonets, so that rust continues to spread and the leather scabbards dry out, shrink and crack. Others polish, grind and buff everything they own, in the misguided conviction that however good an example they have acquired, they can still improve it. These people fall into two categories: those who hate bright steel, and either paint or blue every surface, and those who prefer to polish a blued scabbard until it gleams with a silvery sheen. Fortunately, they are in a minority, but they are not that uncommon. The greatest problem, indeed the only problem, is not that of knowing what to do, but when to stop. More lasting damage has been done to antique arms by bad restoration than by wear, rust and corrosion put together.

Whatever your personal view, it is worth considering fellow collectors' opinions in case one day you try to exchange one item for another, or are even compelled to sell your collection. The majority do not approve of reblueing and many object to repainted scabbards. Reblueing can make a bayonet virtually unsaleable. It is very rarely well done, even more rarely matches the original colour, and usually leaves a lingering and instantly recognisable smell.

## Blades

The blade is often the most difficult part to clean to a really satisfactory finish, and the best advice is not to attempt to remove surface pitting caused by rust. I once saw a bayonet that had been professionaly ground to an excellent surface, but in order to leave the factory markings close to the crossguard, the first 25mm (1in) or so had been left in a quite deeply pitted state. It would certainly have been wrong to remove those important marks, but the overall effect was pointless. Most blades do have some rust on them, even if it is only light surface staining, and the aim must be to remove it without at the same time rubbing or grinding away the metal.

Time, care and a light touch will restore most blades, but many dealers resort to power tools for cleaning. These machines, especially the industrial grinders, have damaged more antique arms than anything else. In the 1960s one dealer always had a wonderful display of gleaming weapons, the brass glittered like gold, and the blades reflected light like mirrors. Unfortunately, closer examination revealed makers' trademarks, dates, proofmarks and serial numbers all ground away, sharp edges rounded and worse. To improve the look of blued scabbards he would buff the frog studs and the round tips bright – nice contrast, sold better, so he claimed. Perhaps they did sell better, but they were ruined. That said, power tools can clean well without damage, but only if great care is taken. They save hours of tedious work with brass polish or emery paper, but if too much pressure is applied or they are used for too long, then harm will be done.

Even a bench grinder can be used with the right equipment, preferably with soft mops made of layers of cloth stitched together. Different compounds are sold which can be applied to the mops, but only the finest grades should be used.

The harsher ones will remove rust and grind away steel in a shower of sparks. The best come in blocks like large bars of soap and can be bought from some hardware shops. W. Canning Materials Ltd produce a large range of polishing compounds. Surface rust may be removed from blades by running them lengthwise over the wheel, without pressing and without stopping. For this a slightly coarser compound like Satene is required. Care should be taken to avoid catching the crossguard and rounding its edges. Wire wheels may have the same effect if too much pressure is applied, whereas with care they too can be a great help.

Parkerised blades such as those of the later British Patterns 1907 and 1913 bayonets usually need washing in paraffin to remove any caked-on oil or grease; then fine wire wool will clean the surface to its original matt grey without damage. A power tool can be used to good effect, but all that is required is to wet the blade in paraffin, then run a wire wheel down its length again without pressure and without interruption. A single pass is enough to clean most blades; much more and the surface will be damaged beyond restoration.

Blued blades must be treated with great care, and the use of any power tools should be avoided. Fine wire wool together with oil or paraffin will remove most rust spots or stains. Raised rust patches should be pushed off, not scraped, using a smooth blunt instrument like the back of a knife. The slightest surface scratch will always show on a blued blade. Oil the rust well before removing it, then clean the area with more oil and the finest grade wire wool.

## Hilts

Hilts may be divided into four basic groups: brass, steel with chequered leather grips, steel with removable wood grips, and brass or steel with permanently attached wood grips. Brass hilts like those of the French Models 1842 and 1866 sabre bayonets are the easiest to clean, but if they are badly tarnished, never use battery acid or even vinegar on them. It is possible to use either method with success, but the hilt is often left for too long in the corrosive liquid, and the surface, although clean, is pitted and dull. Both liquids are difficult to neutralise when they seep behind the press stud springs. Again, fine wire wool will remove even the worst greenish black verdigris, and the finish can be restored with any commercial brass polish. It may be time-consuming, but there is no risk of damage.

Power tools with soft brushes or mops will also clean brass well, but best of all are the small brushes used by dental technicians which are also sold in kits to model makers. These tiny brushes will clean between the hilt ribs or in awkward places, where, for example, the blade meets the crossguard. Brass hilts are best well cleaned and polished, then left alone except for the occasional wipe with a duster. Polishing always removes some metal, and will eventually round edges and remove markings. Clear furniture or shoe polish preserves the finish well. Lacquering also protects but discolours after a while. It used to be difficult to remove, but modern solvents will do so without harming the metal.

Hilts with wooden grips secured by rivets are the hardest to clean. Don't try to remove them, but protect the edges with masking tape when cleaning the adjoining steel. Similarly, British chequered leather grips should be left in place. In theory they can be removed because the rivets are in fact friction pins which can be punched out. It is not all that difficult to do so, but replacing them is another matter. I have never seen it done well. Both types of hilt are hard to clean with a power tool, and masking tape is little protection against a powerful wire wheel. Fine-grade emery paper in thin strips pulled back and forth across the surface will clean off most surface rust, provided the hilt is held steady. Use either lead spacers or thick leather or wood blocks in the vice to grip the blade. For flat surfaces on the back of the hilt and pommel, wrap the emery paper tightly around a wood block to avoid rounding the edges.

Emery polishing paper will remove light scratches and restore the finish of bright steel. The press studs should be removed whenever possible, and cleaned and oiled before reassembling. In general, early French press studs cannot be taken apart because the leaf springs are riveted in place. The press stud on their M 1842/59 may be taken to bits by undoing a small screw on the side, but as the V-spring is within the hilt it is impossible to put it together again, so leave well alone. The springs on British and German bayonets can be removed by undoing the retaining screws. More modern press studs with internal coiled springs unscrew, but they are difficult to grip. Normal pliers will bite into the steel and damage the surface, so either wrap a piece of cloth around the stud or use a very old pair of pipe pliers with worn, rounded teeth.

For the few studs that will not turn, some penetrating oil followed by a tap with a mallet or piece of wood will loosen the rust's grip on the thread.

Steel hilts with detachable grips are simpler to clean, but produce more problems. British bayonets from the P 1888 Mk III and German bayonets from 1898 onwards were all fitted with grips secured by bolts and round nuts. The nuts all have a cut across their centre for a screwdriver, but the end of the bolt in the centre prevents the use of a normal tool. I possessed three different screwdrivers modified to fit the different-sized nuts simply by filing away the centres to leave two prongs of the correct size and width. The British bolts are easier to remove because the round domed heads are cut with a screwdriver slot. The German bolts, on the other hand, have plain domed heads and the edges are ribbed to grip the surrounding wood. However, as these heads rarely turn, the nuts can be undone with the right type of screwdriver. It is still sensible to use penetrating oil first, and to tap the nut to break any rust seal on the thread. Do not force the bolts out of the grips. The German ones will come free, but the heads often emerge taking small pieces of surrounding wood with them. To avoid this, drill a block of wood with holes of the same diameters as the bolt heads. Place the grip on the block with the bolt directly over one of the holes, then tap it free. The block will support the grip wood and prevent damage.

Rust and dirt should be removed from the grips by washing them in paraffin before lightly oiling the undersides and replacing them. Rust may build up under the grips, and often has to be scraped off the wood. The steel beneath the grips can be cleaned with a wire brush or wire wool, but trademarks were often stamped on the tangs, so care should be taken. A bench power tool is a great help at this stage. Press stud parts and bolts can be held against a rotating wire brush and the threads cleaned at a touch. It may be obvious, but goggles and a mask should always be worn, particularly with wire brushes.

The one-piece wood grip on the earliest German S 98 is extremely difficult to remove. It is probably best left alone because it will crack in two if forced off the tang. The only safe way to remove it is to tap the tang from the grip. A block of wood is required with a groove cut to the width of the tang and wide enough to support the grip edges. Placed upside down on the block by carefully tapping the pommel, the tang should enter the groove and the grip be preserved in one piece.

Once the bayonet has been cleaned, do avoid greasing the blade. As with brass, clear wax polish will give a layer of protection. If wax is not used, the occasional wipe with an oily cloth will keep rust at bay provided it is always done after anyone handles the bayonet. Fingerprints on a clean blade will quickly form a rust pattern. The rust can easily be removed, but the steel will remain stained. A few collectors keep two or three pairs of thin gloves for guests to wear before handling their collection. It may sound a little fussy to do so, but it does prevent rust and saves a lot of time spent cleaning.

## Scabbards and Belt Frogs

Steel scabbards are the simplest to clean, but before starting it is important to find out how the steel was originally finished. Many were polished bright, but others were blued, parkerised or painted. Original paint should be preserved when possible, but if rust is present under the paint and spreading, it should be removed. A commercial paint stripper will remove all the old surface, but will have to be neutralised according to the instructions on the container. Once the rust has also been cleaned from the surface, the scabbard must be dried thoroughly, and wiped clean with white spirits. Black-painted scabbards, especially those of German walking-out bayonets, can be repainted using the aerosol sprays on sale in any garage. The simplest method is to grip a screwdriver or tyre lever in a vice, then slide the scabbard onto it. The metal can be sprayed and the scabbard turned without touching it. An undercoat will give a stronger finish whereas a single topcoat, although looking the part, will scratch easily, exposing the metal. Ideally one should own up to repainting if the bayonet is sold or exchanged.

The all-steel German ersatz hilts and their scabbards were originally painted field-grey or occasionally black. Very few have survived in this state, but if much of the German paint is still evident, it should be preserved carefully. Again oil and fine wire wool may be used to remove any rust which might spread, and the paint wiped with an oily cloth to remove surface dirt. Many of these bayonets have been used by the Turkish army, and in some cases blued overall. In my view, repainting with the field-grey paint available from model shops is acceptable. It improves the appearance, conserves the steel and prevents rust. It may be a reproduction finish, but there is no lasting harm as it can easily be removed with a solvent. However, buying a bayonet which has been repainted should be approached with caution. At best the paint will be a surface covering, but at worst it may cover hidden faults. Deep pitting on hilts can easily be filled before painting, as can Turkish numerals and small dents and bruises.

Once again the decision to paint or not is a personal matter. As a dealer, I never painted the stock I had for sale nor did I like buying repainted bayonets. However, I did restore some of my private collection in the manner described.

Steel scabbards originally issued with a bright finish may be cleaned using any of the methods described for blades, depending on the amount of dirt and rust present. Blued steel should only be cleaned with fine wire wool soaked in paraffin or oil. Again rust spots should be pushed off, not scraped. There is nothing worse than badly rusted scabbards that have been reblued. A dull blue finish over pitting looks as false at it is.

Most German scabbards have detachable mouthpieces with attached blade-retaining springs. Whenever possible, these should be removed and the springs cleaned, for although the springs were usually galvanised, wear from the blades has often left bare metal which rusts easily. There is little point in carefully cleaning a blade, then discovering weeks later that rusty patches have developed from the uncleaned springs. A single screw secures the mouthpiece in place, and light taps with a wooden mallet will usually free it. Unfortunately, the majority of scabbards have their mouthpieces permanently riveted in position. Dirt and grease accumulate in the tip, and although I have read that heating the metal over a flame will dissolve the grease, I have never found this method necessary. Poking a piece of strong wire, taken from a cut and straightened clothes hanger, down the scabbard will eventually dislodge the dirt. It can take time, so patience rather than skill is all that is required.

Leather scabbards with brass or steel mounts are more difficult to clean. Much damage is caused by the atmosphere of centrally heated rooms which dries out the leather, resulting in shrinkage, broken seams and flaking surfaces. It is not advisable to remove the mounts which were usually glued in place before the staples were added; nor is it difficult to take out the staples, but they break easily, and are very hard to put back. Italian top mounts are the exception because once the large screw close to the frog stud is removed, the mount slides off for cleaning. Brass and steel mounts can be cleaned as already described and a narrow strip of emery paper is essential for working around and beneath the frog studs.

Many scabbards cleaned by power tools have thin staples ground down to the point where they break. An even more common fault is to find the leather badly scuffed by wire wheels where it meets the mounts. Masking tape is not advisable on leather. Any self-adhesive paper or tape, even price stickers, will lift the surface of a dry scabbard when removed. On polished leather, even in good condition, a label will leave a matt rectangle or circle which is very difficult to polish out. Dry flaking leather should be treated with a leather preservative, and several applications may be needed before the surface can be repolished. Saddle soap will clean as well as restore, provided the instructions are followed, but on no account should neatsfoot oil be used. It was once employed as a preservative, but scabbards and belt frogs treated with this oil grow a fine white mould, and heavy deposits of verdigris form around the brass or copper rivets and on the top mount if it too is brass. Once some suppleness has been restored to the leather, normal shoe polish will give a perfect finish.

I have never seen a scabbard well repaired when the stitching at the back has broken and the leather has opened, and I would prefer to clean it and leave well alone. Nor have I seen a shrunken scabbard restored to its original length. Sometimes the treatment already described will help by giving some suppleness to the leather. A few professional restorers are capable of replacing complete scabbard leathers, but this should only be a last resort – perhaps when a scabbard is completely broken in one or two places.

Leather belt frogs may be treated in the same way as scabbards although many buff leather frogs were produced with the rough side facing out like suede, and these were never intended to be polished. Stitching can be repaired using thick thread and a saddler's needle. Take extra care with Japanese belt frogs because their straps are often brittle, and frequently break when they are unbuckled. Buff leather British frogs are often dirty and covered in old dry blanco which dissolves easily in warm water, allowing the leather to be scrubbed clean. This often reveals old unit markings on the backs. Dry them naturally and slowly and use tennis white to restore the colour if required. Some buff frogs in use since the war were not blancoed but painted white, and these are best brushed clean. Similarly, webbing belt frogs can be scrubbed in warm water and rinsed clean without causing any damage. Care should be taken to check that the frogs are completely dry before fitting them on their scabbards, otherwise rust will develop out of sight.

## Displaying a Collection

The most attractive method of display must be that used by some museums where the bayonets are set out within glass-fronted mahogany cases. Each bayonet is secured to the background by brass loops screwed in place, and each has a printed identification label. However, not only is this very expensive, but the bayonets cannot be moved or examined without difficulty.

For various reasons, security, personal taste or lack of space, many collectors prefer to store their bayonets out of sight, in cupboards, boxes and trunks. There are two disadvantages to this; first, unless each bayonet is carefully wrapped, some damage, however slight, will occur when they are placed on top of each other. Wood grips will be bruised and scabbard paint scratched or chipped, but most importantly, as they are hidden from view, rust may develop before it is noticed. No matter how well an item is cleaned and protected, there may still be damp in the scabbard leather or belt frog which reacts in contact with the metal. Unseen condensation can build up, and the rust only discovered when the bayonets are unwrapped.

The ideal method is to keep the collection in shallow drawers. Old chart cabinets are perfect. The collection is hidden from casual visitors, but can be shown to interested friends with ease. The contents can also be checked regularly. If the collection is to be displayed on a wall, a permanent set-up like those used in museums is best avoided. New bayonets will be found that complete a set or need hanging with similar types, so some thought has to be given to the flexibility or movement of the collection. Pegboard was once popular, and is still used by some collectors. A whole wall or a complete room can be lined, but it does mean attaching a number of battens to the walls, rawlplugged and screwed in place. More battens have to be added behind the board to support the weight and hold it firmly in place. The hooks are readily available, although quite expensive, and can be used to display the bayonets horizontally. Wire coat hangers may be cut and bent to make awkwardly shaped hooks as required. The most impressive use of pegboard in a private collection has the whole surface covered in hessian and the borders framed by strips of wood. Alternatively, the board can be painted to match the surrounding walls.

A much simpler method, and equally impressive visually, is to have the bayonets hanging vertically in rows, one above the other. All this requires is long battens fixed across the wall. The upper slim edge of each batten has small nails spaced according to the width of the bayonet hanging from it. A piece of string, picture wire or strong fishing line can be passed through the belt frog, then hooked over the nail. Belt frogs are now too valuable to be distorted or cut by wire, so place a short piece of slim plastic tubing through the belt loop, cut it to the precise width, and pass the wire through the tube first. This will prevent damage and keep the frog in its original shape. Any tube can be used, the sort available from DIY stores for enclosing electrical wires, the cardboard centres from adding machine tapes, or even old ballpoint pens once the empty ink container has been discarded.

Private collections are rarely designed as permanent displays. The bayonets are shown to other collectors, taken down, examined and rehung, then they are moved and rearranged again and again.

# BIBLIOGRAPHY

Most titles currently in print are available from the author at Tharston Press, Morton Hall, Norwich, Norfolk NR9 5JS

Calamandrei, Cesare, *Baionette Italiane*, Editoriale Olimpia, Italy, 1992

Carter, Anthony, *German Bayonets,Volume I, The Models 98/02 and 98/05*, Tharston Press, Norfolk, 1984

Carter, Anthony, *German Bayonets, Volume II, The Models 71/84, 69/98, AS 71/98, kS 98, 1914 and 84/98*, Tharston Press, 1991

Carter, Anthony, *German Bayonets,Volume III, The Ersatz, Requisitioned and Captured Bayonets*, Tharston Press, 1992

Carter, Anthony, *German Bayonets, Volume IV, The Regulation Pattern Sword Bayonets 1860–1900*, Tharston Press, 1995

Evans, R.D.C., *British Bayonet Letters Patent 1721–1961*, Published by the author, Shipley, 1991

Janzen, Jerry L., *Bayonets of the Remington Cartridge Period,* Cedar Ridge Publications, Oklahoma, USA, 1993

Janzen, Jerry L., *Bayonets from Janzen's Notebook,* Tulsa, Oklahoma, 1987

Johnson, Larry, *Japanese Bayonets*, Cedar Ridge Publications, Oklahoma, USA, 1988

Priest, Graham, *The Brown Bess Bayonet 1720–1860*, Tharston Press, 2nd edition, 1995

Reilly, Robert M., *American Socket Bayonets and Scabbards*, Andrew Mowbray Inc., Rhode Island, USA, 1990

Skennerton, Ian D. and Richardson, Robert, *British & Commonwealth Bayonets*, Margate, Australia, 1986

Skennerton, Ian D., *The British Spike Bayonet*, Margate, Australia, 1982

Smid, Jan and Moudry, Peter, *Bodaky Habsburske Monarchie 1683–1918, Bayonets – Habsburg Monarchy,* Ars-Arm Prague, 1994

Walker, Gary L. and Weinand, R.J., *German Clamshells and Other Bayonets,* Quincy, Illinois, USA, 1985

## Out of Print

Carter, Anthony, *German Ersatz Bayonets*, The Lyon Press, Brighton, 1976

Carter, Anthony and Walter, John, *The Bayonet, A History of Knife and Sword Bayonets 1850–1970*, Arms & Armour Press, London, 1974

Carter, Anthony, *Allied Bayonets of World War 2*, Arms & Armour Press, London, 1969

Carter, Anthony, *Bayonet Belt Frogs Parts I & II*, Tharston Press, 1983

Evans, R.D.C., and Stephens, F.J., *The Bayonet, An Evolution and History*, Militaria Publications, Milton Keynes, 1985

Hardin, Albert N., *The American Bayonet 1776–1964*, Philadelphia, USA, 1977

Kärhä, Reino, *Russian & Soviet Bayonets*, Helsinki, Finland, 1975

Kiesling, Paul, *Bayonets of the World*, 4 volumes, Military Collectors Service, Netherlands, 1972–6

Skennerton, Ian D., *Australian Service Bayonets*, Margate, Australia, 1986

Walter, John, *The German Bayonet 1871–1945*, Arms & Armour Press, London, 1976

Watts, John and White, Peter, *The Bayonet Book*, Birmingham, 1975

Wilkinson-Latham, R.J., *British Military Bayonets from 1700 to 1945*, Hutchinson, London, 1967

## Current Journals

*The Armourer*, Beaumont Publishing

*Deutsche Waffen Journal*, Journal-Verlag Schwend GmbH, Schwäbish Hall

*Gazette des Armes*, Paris

*Guns Review*, Ravenhill Publishing Co. Ltd., London

*International Arms & Militaria Collector*, Arms & Militaria Press, Australia

*Military Illustrated*, Publishing News Ltd

*Classic Arms & Militaria*, Peterson Publications

# PRICE GUIDE FOR 1996/7

The bayonets included in this guide are those that the beginner or general collector can reasonably expect to find, and whose prices have stabilised over the years. British and German bayonets have been given comparatively more attention than other sections because these two fields are most widely collected in Europe. The majority of exceptionally rare bayonets have not been included as insufficient examples have been found and resold to establish known values.

The prices given are those that a collector can reasonably expect to pay to a reputable dealer for a good clean example, complete with its scabbard. Prices realised at auctions have been published in several books, but these figures have little meaning. One general guide includes values as low as 10% of those regularly charged and paid, while another prints figures many years out of date. Too many factors affect auction prices for them to be a reliable guide. On any given day two collectors wanting the same lot may push an item well over its normal level, while the absence of one collector on the same day might result in a sale price well below its true market value.

It must be stressed that the values given are the retail prices in the United Kingdom. As a rule, all bayonets are of greatest value in their country of origin where there are more collectors searching for items relating to their own national history. The wholesale value or the sum you may expect to be paid for a bayonet is considerably less. In most fields of antiques this is often less than half the price charged in the dealer's shop or catalogue. For example, established dealers will be registered for Value Added Tax at 17.5%, and a profit margin of 33% is generally considered fair, if not on the low side. Consequently, a bayonet sold for £100 is actually about £85 plus tax. A third profit on the £85 results in the wholesale value of about £57.

The investment side of collecting must be thought of in the long term; preferably at least ten years. The only real reason for collecting anything must be the pleasure of the hunt, and finally ownership. The probable increase in value must be regarded as a bonus. That said, my catalogues of the mid-1970s were listing many bayonets for £12 and £15 which are now each worth several hundreds, and in some cases more than £500.

Firm values cannot be given for all bayonets, especially some of those produced since the last war. Although most bayonets except the most common have risen steadily in value over the past decade, a few have not. The most dramatic drop in values has been for the post-war bayonets of the Soviet Union and its allies in the Warsaw Pact. The 1990/1 edition of this book warned against paying high prices for any bayonet in current use. It might be desirable to be the first collector to own an example of a recently introduced bayonet, and it would certainly be a good talking point, but its value will plummet when it becomes obsolete. The fall of the Berlin Wall has resulted in hundreds if not thousands of Warsaw Pact bayonets being sold to collectors at prices a fraction of those charged a few years ago; some £150 bayonets now sell for as little as £15 or £20.

The 1990/1 edition listed the recent import of thousands of French Model 1886 Lebel bayonets, Portuguese M 1886 and British P 1887s. To those must be added the Australian Owen SMG bayonets, the Soviet bayonets already mentioned, the Swedish M 1896 and Portuguese SMG bayonets.

Condition is extremely important, and the text refers to its effect on values. Common bayonets that are readily available have no value at all in poor condition, and it is always preferable to purchase good clean examples of even the rarest bayonets, especially if resale is ever considered. While it is understandable that a collector should wish to fill a gap with a representative specimen, however poor, it must be stressed that it may have little or no value to other collectors. Generally, the rarer the bayonet, the more acceptable it is to have a well-used or worn specimen, but I would hesitate to place a commercial value on such items for, as prices rise, collectors become more and more discriminating.

The rare bayonets, particularly the early to mid-nineteenth century British and German sword bayonets, are also difficult to value with any precision. The figures given are only guides, and the frequent use of a plus sign indicates that on occasions higher prices have been paid. Most dealers know who is searching for the very rare bayonets, and if they have a customer waiting, one who wants the particular item badly, they will pay over the odds to acquire it, resulting in a higher than usual asking price. The only limits are set by collectors who have to decide for themselves whether a certain figure is too much to pay for a bayonet that they may have spent ten or twenty years searching for to no avail. In general dealers will not attach ridiculous prices to very rare items unless they have paid too much themselves. So whereas the dealer is motivated by the need to make a profitable sale, the collector who sometimes pays over the odds does so from the urge to acquire and keep the item concerned.

## LIST OF ABBREVIATIONS

### Rarity rating

R1    Common bayonets recently imported or sold in large numbers.
R2    Common bayonets wholesaled in large numbers a few years ago but no longer available in quantities.
R3    Quite common; single bayonets readily available.
R4    Becoming scarce in good condition.
R5    Scarce in good condition.
R6    Rarer but still available if expensive.
R7    Rare and difficult to find.

R8   Very rare and hard to find. Often very expensive.
R9   Very rare with less than 10 known examples sold within the last 5 years.
R10  Extremely rare; only 2 or 3 examples sold within the last 5 years.
R11  Almost unigue; one recorded example sold.

## Rarity value

NRV  No rarity value. Poor examples virtually worthless.
RV   Rarity value. Even poor specimens can command quite high prices.

## Condition

EC   Excellent condition with all original finish.
VGC  Very good clean condition.

# VALUES 1996/97

## Argentina

**1** Model 1891 Bayonet: alloy grips R2;
NRV; about £30. Brass grips R3/4; £45,
many imported, now common with or
without original markings.

## Australia

**2** Pattern 1944 Owen SMG Bayonet: R1;
NRV; many recently imported; £15.
**3** Pattern 1944 Machete Bayonet Mk I:
R6; £200+. Fakes are now on the market
so great care should be taken.
**4** Pattern 1944 Machete Bayonet Mk II:
R9; £300+.

## Austria

**5** Model 1867 Sabre Bayonet: R8/9; RV;
normally with chequered leather grips and
steel scabbard; as illustrated with staghorn
grips, R11; £250; normal type £100+.
**6** Model 1867 Bayonet: R4; officially
shortened blade and scabbard; about £80.
**7** Model 1870 Bayonet: R4; about £80.
**8** Model 1870 NCO's Bayonet: R7; RV,
about £95.
**9** Model 1873 Bayonet: R5; about £90.
**10** Model 1873 Bayonet with wood grips:
R5/6; £90.
**11** Model 1888 Knife Bayonet: R4; NRV;
about £45. Add 50% for rare Bulgarian
crowned 'F' marking.

**12** Model 1888 NCO's Knife Bayonet:
R5; about £55.
**13** Model 1895 Gendarmerie Bayonet: R9;
RV; £200.
**14** Model 1895 Knife Bayonet: R3; NRV;
about £30.
**15** Model 1895 NCO's Knife Bayonet:
R4; NRV; £35. Add about £5 for good,
clean bayonet knot.
**16** Model 1895 Carbine NCO's Knife
Bayonet: as shown R9/10 with enamel
regimental badge, £75, fakes with spurious
badges have been recorded recently; without badge, R4, NRV, about £35.
**17** Model 1895 Carbine Knife Bayonet:
R3; NRV; many minor variations of the
foresight; about £30.
**18** Model 1888 Ersatz Bayonet: R7; RV;
£150.
**19** Model 1895 Ersatz Bayonet: R7; RV;
£150.
**20** Ersatz Bayonet: R5; crude original finish; variations; about £95.
**21** Ersatz Bayonet: R5; variations; about
£75. Modern fakes do exist, usually blued
and better finished than the originals.

## Belgium

**22** Model 1868 Pioneer Bayonet: R6;
usually VGC-EC, £300+.
**23** Model 1888 Pioneer Bayonet: R7;

NRV as most are near EC; £250.

**24** Model 1882 Epée Bayonet: R8; RV; £200 for VGC example.

**25** Model 1882 Bandsman's Bayonet: R10; RV; £250.

**26** Model 1889 Sword Bayonet: R9; RV; £250.

**27** Model 1889 Civil Guard Bayonet: R8; RV; £95.

**28** Model 1889 Infantry Bayonet: R4; about £60. £100+ for rare examples made in England by Sanderson Brothers & Newbould.

**29** Model 1889 made in the USA by Hopkins & Allen: R5/6; without steel scabbard about £75. Double if complete with extremely rare scabbard.

**30** Model 1916 Epée Bayonet: R4; NRV; £40-50.

**31** Model 1916 Gendarmerie Bayonet; R8; RV; £100.

**32** Model 1924 Epée Bayonet: R4; NRV; about £45.

**Canada**

**33** Model 1893 Bayonet: R9; RV; £300+.

**34** Ross Bayonet Mk I: R4; NRV; about £100. 10% less with later added US markings.

**35** Ross Bayonet Mk II: R3; NRV; several variations; about £50. R9 if British marked; £200+.

**36** C1 Bayonet: R3; NRV; EC only £50.

**China**

**37** German Model 1871 Bayonet exported to China: R8; RV; Chinese markings; no German date or cypher; £150.

**38** Belgian-made Bayonet, c1920: R4; NRV; several minor variations; scabbards are very rare; about £50-85 without scabbard.

**39** Type 53 (SKS) Folding Bayonet: R3/4 in VGC; NRV, about £35.

**40** Type 53 (SKS) Folding Bayonet: R4; NRV, about £35.

**41** Type 56 (AK) Folding Bayonet: R4; NRV, about £35.

**Denmark**

**42** Model 1867 Sabre Bayonet: R4; NRV; prices vary greatly; about £75–85. Add 15% for later variation with coiled spring press-stud instead of leaf spring.

**43** Model 1889 Knife Bayonet: R4/5; NRV, about £75–85 for earliest type with chequered leather grips or wood grips as shown.

**44** Model 1915 Bayonet: R5; about £125.

**France**

**45** Model 1840 Sabre Bayonet: R9; RV; £400+.

**46** Model 1842 Sabre Bayonet: R4; NRV; £95.

**47** Model 1842/59 Sabre Bayonet: R5; NRV; VGC only £75.

**48** Model 1866 Sabre Bayonet: R3/4; NRV; £35 if made at St Etienne, Tulle, Châtellerault or Mutzig Arsenals. About £45 if made by Stehelin & Cie or Herdecke, £90-100 if made in England.

**49** Model 1866 Socket Bayonet: R7; £100. Add 50% with scabbard.

**50** Model 1874 Epée Bayonet: R3; NRV; about £45-60 if made at St Etienne, Tulle or Châtellerault Arsenals. Add 15% if marked Paris-Oudry, L. Deny-Paris or Usine de Steyr.[1]

**51** Model 1878 Kropatschek Bayonet: R8; RV; anchor mark on crossguard, blade, inscription of Mre de Steyr – Mre de Werndl and date; £200.[1]

**52** Model 1886 Epée Bayonet: R3; NRV; about £45.[1]

**53** Model 1886/15 Epée Bayonet: R5; NRV; £40.[1]

**54** Model 1890 Gendarmerie Bayonet: R7; RV; VGC about £150+.[1]

**55** Model 1895 Daudeteau Bayonet: R9; RV; VGC £150+.[1]

**56** Model 1886/93/16 Bayonet with brass hilt: R2; NRV; brass or white metal hilts; EC only about £35.[1]

**57** Model 1886/93/16 Bayonet with blued steel hilt: R3; NRV; £45.[1]

**58** Model 1886/93/16/35 Bayonet: R4; NRV; usually about £35. All M 1886 bayonets can be found with blades officially shortened in 1935.[1]

**59** Model 1892 Bayonet: R3/4; NRV; £55.[1]

**60** Model 1892/15 Bayonet: R3/4; NRV; £45.[1]

**61** Model 1892 Bayonet: R3/4; NRV; later type with wide muzzle ring; £40 for VGC+ examples. About £100 if stamped with original French blade inscription.[1]

**62** Model 1914 Bayonet: R4/5; made by Remington in the USA; about £85. Add 20% if stamped with original French serial number.

**63** Model 1936 MAS Rod Bayonet: R1; NRV; variations in chequering; about £15.

**64** Model 1949/56 MAS Knife Bayonet: R2; NRV; EC only about £35.

## Germany

**65** Prussian Model 1860 Fusilier Bayonet: R8; RV; VGC about £450+.

**66** Prussian Model 1865 Jaeger Bayonet: R7/8; RV; VGC about £450+.

**67** Prussian Model 1865 Pioneer Bayonet: R8/9; RV; VGC £500+.

**68** Bavarian Model 1869 Bayonet: R8; RV; hilts often modified; £385.

**69** Prussian Model 1871 Infantry Bayonet: R5; about £125 for VGC. Add 25% for Bavarian example, 40% for Saxon example and 15% for rarer steel scabbard.

**70** Prussian Model 1871 Infantry NCO's Bayonet: R7; RV; about £300. Similar variations to above.

**71** Prussian Model 1871 Jaeger Bayonet: R7/8; RV; VGC about £450+.

**72** Bavarian Model 1871 Pioneer Bayonet: R10; RV; £550+.

**73** Württemberg Model 1871 Pioneer Bayonet: R10; RV; £600.

**74** Prussian Model 1871 Walking Out Bayonet: R4; NRV; purchased privately; about £125.

**75** Prussian Model 1871 NCO's Walking Out Bayonet: R6; RV; about £175.

**76** Prussian Model 1871 Jaeger Walking Out Bayonet: R7; RV; £150.

**77** Model 1860/98 Bayonet: R8/9; RV; rehilted Model 1860; about £400+.

**78** Model 1869/98 Bayonet: R8; RV; rehilted Bavarian Model 1869; about £350.

**79** Model 1869/98 Bayonet: R10; RV; rehilted Bavarian Model 1869 NCO's bayonet; £500+.

**80** Model 1871/84 Knife Bayonet: R4/5; NRV; £90.[2]

**81** Model 1871/84 Knife Bayonet: R4/5; NRV; with short fullers; £90. Add 15% for Bavarian markings, 30% for Saxon.[2]

**82** Model 1871/84 NCO's Knife Bayonet: R10; RV; Bavarian markings only; VGC £500+.[2]

**83** Model 1884/98 Knife Bayonet: R4; NRV; two variations with short and long fullers; VGC only £75.[2]

**84** Short Model 1898 Knife Bayonet (kS 98): R5/6; RV; chequered leather grips with three rivets about £125. Some fakes encountered made by reworking 3rd Reich versions.

**85** Short Model 1898 Knife Bayonet (kS 98): R6; RV; wood grips about £140; composition grips about £250.

**86** Model 1898 Bayonet, 1st pattern with one-piece wood grip: R5; NRV; £125.[3]

**87** Model 1898 NCO's Bayonet, 1st pattern: R7; RV; about £275.[3]

**88** Model 1898 Bayonet, 2nd pattern with two-piece grips: R4; NRV; about £80.[3]

**89** Model 1898 NCO's Bayonet, 2nd pattern: R6/7; RV; about £200+.[3]

**90** Model 1898/02 Bayonet: R8; RV; £450+. Prussian most common followed by Bavarian and Saxon.

**91** Model 1898/05 Bayonet, 1st pattern: R3/4; NRV; £60.

**92** Model 1898/05 Saw-Backed Bayonet, 1st pattern: R4/5; NRV; £100.

**93** Model 1898/05 Bayonet, 2nd pattern: R3; NRV; depending on markings £45.

**94** Model 1898/05 Saw-Backed Bayonet, 2nd pattern: R4; NRV; £80.

**95** Model 1898/05 with saw-back removed: 1st pattern R8; about £125. 2nd pattern R4; NRV; £60.

**96** Model 1914 Bayonet: Several minor variations; R4; NRV; £50+.

**97** Model 1914 Bayonet: Made by Bayard; R5; NRV; £75.

**98** Model 1914 Saw-Backed Bayonet: Made by Samsonwerk; R6; NRV; £150+. Add 20% for other rarer makers.

**99** Bavarian Model 1914 Bayonet: R5/6; about £150.

**100** Bavarian Model 1914 Saw-Backed Bayonet: R10; RV; £500+.

**101** Ersatz Combination Knife Bayonet: R4/5; VGC only about £125. Indian-made reproductions now on the market. No value.

**102** Ersatz Combination Knife Bayonet: R8; RV; VGC; £350+.

**103** Ersatz Bayonet: R2/3; NRV; fullered blade £35, plain blade £40.

**104** Ersatz Bayonet: R7; cleaning hole on back of hilt; £75+.

**105** Ersatz Bayonet: R2/3; NRV; £35.

**106** Ersatz Bayonet: R9; RV; £350+.

**107** Ersatz Bayonet: R6/7; brass hilt; RV; £150.

**108** Ersatz Bayonet: R3; many slight variations; fullered blade £40, plain blade £45.

**109** Ersatz Bayonet: R7; RV, £65.

**110** Ersatz Bayonet: R7; RV; plain blade £60, fullered about £85.

**111** Ersatz Bayonet: R4/5; NRV; fullered or plain blade about £50.

**112** Ersatz Bayonet: R3; NRV; any variation about £45.

**113** Ersatz Bayonet: R4; about £90.

**114** Ersatz Bayonet: R6; about £125+.

**115** Ersatz Bayonet: R4; £90.

**116** Ersatz Bayonet: R2/3; £35.

**117** Ersatz Bayonet: R4; fullered blade £40, plain £55; variation with brass hilt £125++.

**118** Ersatz Bayonet: R7; about £250.

**119** Ersatz Bayonet: R9; £450+.

**120** Ersatz Bayonet: R8; about £250.

**121** Ersatz Bayonet: R8; about £250.

**122** Ersatz Bayonet: R9/10; RV; £450+.

**123** Ersatz Bayonet: R8; RV; £400.

**124** Ersatz Bayonet: R7/8; RV; £400.

**125** Ersatz Bayonet: R10; RV; £420+. Add at least 10% for any bayonet with unit markings. Subtract at least 50% for examples shortened to 250mm (9.85in) by the Turks in the 1930s.

**126** Model 1884/98 Knife Bayonet: 1915–18 production; R3/4; NRV; £40.

**127** Model 1884/98 Saw-Backed Knife Bayonet: 1915-18; R4; NRV; about £75; with saw-back removed about £55.

**128** Model 1884/98 Knife Bayonet: 3rd Reich; R2, NRV; about £35. Expensive fakes with modern saw-backs cut into the blades have been encounted.

**129** Model 1884/98 Knife Bayonet: 3rd Reich; R2; NRV; about £35-45. Add 40% for jwh code of Châtellerault Arsenal in Occupied France.

**130** Czech Model 1924 Bayonet: 3rd Reich; R3/4; no muzzle ring; German markings; slight variations; about £35.

**Greece**

**131** Model 1874 Bayonet: Identical to the French M 1874 but inscribed Waffenfabrik Steyr and dated; R4; NRV; about £55.

**132** Model 1874/03 Bayonet: Muzzle ring replaced by one to fit the Model 1903 rifle; R6; RV; about £95.

**133** Model 1874/03 Bayonet: Modification variation; R6; RV; about £95.

**134** Model 1903 Bayonet: made at Steyr; R5; scabbards are rarer; without scabbard £55, with £75, made in Italy by Eredi Gnutti, Brescia £125 and £135 with the rarer steel scabbard.

**135** Model 1903 Bayonet: converted from a Model 1874; R7; RV; about £80 without scabbard and £125 with.

**136** Model 1903 Knife Bayonet: R6; RV; 'G' on blade and St George & Dragon on pommel; VGC about £65.

**Holland**

**137** Model 1873 Beaumont Sabre Bayonet: R6; RV; about £70.

**138** Model 1895 Sword Bayonet: R6; VGC only £75.

**139** Model 1895 Bayonet: R5; NRV; £75; also made with stacking hook £95.

**140** Model 1895 Marine Bayonet: R8 in VGC; about £125.

**141** Model 1895 Cavalry Bayonet: R7; RV; £125.
**142** AR10 Knife Bayonet: R3/4; NRV; VGC only £40.

## India
**143** India Pattern Mk I**: Rl; NRV; about £25.
**144** India Pattern Mk II*: R1; NRV; about £20. Fakes with 17in unfullered blades have been recorded.
**145** India Pattern Mk II: R5 without false edge; RV; £40.
**146** India Pattern Mk III: R2; NRV; about £20. Rare version without the false edge £50+.

## Italy
**147** Model 1870 Sword Bayonet: R4/5; NRV; VGC only about £125.
**148** Model 1870-87 Sword Bayonet: R4/5; NRV; VGC only about £125.
**149** Model 1870 T.S. Bayonet: R8; RV; £250.
**150** Model 1870 T.S. Bayonet: R9; RV; brass hilt; £350.
**151** Model 1870 Shortened Bayonet: R4/5; NRV; several variations; about £40.
**152** Model 1870/15 Knife Bayonet: R3; NRV; several variations; about £40.
**153** Model 1891 Bayonet: R2/3; NRV; produced for fifty years, earliest examples most collected; £35.
**154** Model 1891 Bayonet: R7; RV; brass hilt; VGC about £125.
**155** Model 1891 T.S. Bayonet: R3/4; NRV; about £65.
**156** Model 1938 Folding Bayonet: R3; NRV; VGC only £60.
**157** Model 1938 Beretta Folding Bayonet: R6; £200+.
**158** Model 1938 Modified Bayonet: R2/3; NRV; £40.
**159** Model 1938 Bayonet: R2/3; NRV; £40.

## Japan
**160** Model 1897 Marine Bayonet: R8; RV; £300+.

**161** Model 1897 Bayonet: R2; NRV; about £40. Add at least £150 if stamped with British regimental markings from those purchased by the British Government in 1915.
**162** Model 1897 Bayonet: R2; NRV; about £40. Many cruder variations were produced during the Second World War; most R2 and about £40, but £80 if with rarer wood scabbard, and £150 with rubberised scabbard and attached belt frog.
**163** Model 1911 Folding Bayonet: R5; £120.
**164** Model 1940 SMG Knife Bayonet: R8; RV; prices vary considerably; up to £300+ has been asked. Add about £10 for any original belt frog.

## Norway
**165** Model 1894 Bayonet: R7; some blade variations; VGC about £125. With rare all leather scabbard £160+.
**166** Model 1894 Knife Bayonet: R4; NRV; £75; with rare belt frog about 15% more.

## Portugal
**167** Model 1886 Sword Bayonet: R2; NRV; £45.
**168** Model 1904 Bayonet: R2; NRV; £25.

## Spain
**169** Model 1893 Artillery Bayonet: R2/3; NRV; £35. Examine blades carefully because many were cut in half by the Spanish Government and rewelded together forming blades of unusual lengths.
**170** Model 1893 Knife Bayonet: R2/3; NRV; £25 for both Spanish and German made examples; several variations.
**171** Model 1943 Knife Bayonet: R2/3; NRV; usually marked P.R.8; £25.
**172** Model 1943 Knife Bayonet: R2/3; NRV; variation; £25.
**173** Model 1941 Bolo Bayonet: R1/2; NRV; wood or plastic grips; £15.
**174** Model 1969 CETME Bayonet made for Guatemala, the Spanish Army version

has chequered plastic grips and no fullers in the blade: R3/4, NRV; EC only £45.

## Sweden
**175** Model 1896 Knife Bayonet: R1; NRV; prices vary greatly; £15.
**176** Model 1914 Bayonet: R2/3; NRV; about £60.

## Switzerland
**177** Model 1878 Vetterli Engineers' Bayonet: R5/6; usually EC so NRV; £150.
**178** Model 1914 Schmidt-Rubin Engineers' Bayonet: R3; NRV; VGC+ £85.
**179** Model 1889 Bayonet: R3; NRV; 1st type with plain fullered blade £60+. 2nd type with rivet in fuller about £30. 3rd type with ridge in fuller as shown £40.
**180** Model 1918 Bayonet: R2/3; NRV; EC only about £40.

## Turkey
**181** Model 1874 Socket Bayonet: R5; with scabbard about £95.
**182** Model 1874 Sword Bayonet: R4/5; £125.
**183** Model 1874 Shortened Bayonet: R7; RV; about £75.
**184** Model 1887 Bayonet: R5; NRV; £75.
**185** Model 1890 Bayonet: R4; NRV; about £50.
**186** Model 1890 Band Bayonet: R10; RV; £200+.
**187** Model 1903 Bayonet: R5; VGC about £95. Shortened version in correct scabbard about £50.
**188** Model 1903 Knife Bayonet: R6; £70.
**189** Model 1890 Shortened Bayonet: R6; £35+.
**190** Ersatz Bayonet: R3/4; NRV; £50.
**191** Ersatz Bayonet: R8; RV; £75+. In the 1930s many bayonets were altered, rehilted or shortened; many variations, price range £30+.

## United Kingdom
**192** Brown Bess Socket Bayonet: R3/4; NRV; without scabbard about £75, with scabbard, R8, £125. Reproductions made for re-enactment groups have been recently passed off as originals.
**193** Baker Sword Bayonet, 2nd Pattern: R5; about £150, but £300 with scabbard. Some outright fakes made in India, genuine copies, some with steel hilts, made and used in Nepal; study subject carefully before buying.
**194** Baker Volunteer Sword Bayonet: R8/9; RV; £450 without scabbard, £650 with scabbard.
**195** Volunteer Sword Bayonet: R9; RV; VGC with scabbard £750+.
**196** Volunteer Sword Socket Bayonet: R10; RV; £450+.
**197** New Land Pattern Socket Bayonet: R8; RV; about £150. Add 30% with scabbard.
**198** Pattern 1837 Brunswick Sword Bayonet: R6; rarely found with scabbard; about £300 with scabbard, £150 without.
**199** Constabulary Brunswick Sword Bayonet: R11; RV; as shown £600+.
**200** Pattern 1840 Constabulary Socket Bayonet: R5; VGC with scabbard £125.
**201** Pattern 1842 Socket Bayonet: R3; NRV; about £50; almost double with scabbard. Fakes have been encountered.
**202** Pattern 1843 Sappers & Miners' Sword Socket Bayonet: R8; RV; £250+; almost unknown with scabbard, but add 40% if complete.
**203** East India Company Sword Socket Bayonet: R4/5; NRV; scabbards virtually unknown; VGC about £125. Beware of modern reproductions, no value.
**204** Pattern 1847 Brunswick Sword Bayonet: R4; NRV; about £150; with scabbard £250+.
**205** Pattern 1853 Socket Bayonet: R3; NRV; VGC with scabbard £60 depending on markings. Add 10% if bushed for the Martini-Henry rifle. Fakes have been encountered.
**206** Pattern 1853 Artillery Sword Bayonet: R7/8; RV; VGC £350+.
**207** Pattern 1855 Lancaster Sword Bayonet: R6; about £150 for German-made example, £225+ for British-made version.

**208** Volunteer Sword Bayonet: Steel hilt; R8 in VGC; £350.

**209** Pattern 1856 Sword Bayonet: R3/4; NRV; several variations and unmarked Volunteer examples; all about £70 if VGC and complete. About £100 for Artillery issue with all steel scabbard; add 15% for unit markings and 50% for Whitworth pattern with round attachment bar groove in the pommel.

**210** Pattern 1859 Naval Cutlass Bayonet: R6; VGC and with scabbard about £300. Add at least 25% for the rarer P 1858 with ribbed wood grips covered by leather. Cheap modern reproductions are available, usually with spurious Bleckmann trademark of a bow and arrow; no value.

**211** Volunteer Sword Bayonet: R8; RV; modified from obsolete cutlass bayonets; with scabbard £400. Fakes have been encountered.

**212** Jacobs Sword Bayonet: R8; RV; in great demand; VGC without scabbard about £500; with scabbard up to £800 depending on condition.

**213** Pattern 1871 Elcho Bayonet: R9; RV; also in great demand; from £400 up to £800 depending on condition and with scabbard. Cheap modern reproductions, usually with spurious Alex Coppel's scales trademark or occasionally Elcho Bayonet in an etched panel, have no value.

**214** Pattern 1871 Naval Cutlass Bayonet: R7/8; RV; VGC up to £350.

**215** Pattern 1875 Artillery Bayonet: R6; RV; VGC made in Solingen £250, made at Enfield £400. Add 25% for War Department markings, and £600 for Enfield-made 20.25in (514mm) blade.

**216** Pattern 1876 Socket Bayonet: R3/4; NRV; VGC+ with scabbard £75.

**217** Pattern 1879 Artillery Sword Bayonet: R5; little RV; VGC £200.

**218** Pattern 1887 Mk I Sword Bayonet: R3/4; little RV; £85. Add 10% for brass mounted Indian Army scabbard. The Pattern 1887 Mk II Sword Bayonet (not illustrated), R10; with grips held by two rivets

and with fullered blade has value of at least £300+.

**219** Pattern 1887 Mk III Sword Bayonet: R3; NRV; VGC about £85.

**220** Pattern 1887 Mk IV Sword Bayonet: R3; NRV; VGC about £85.

**221** Pattern 1888 Mk I Bayonet: R7; usually well used; EC examples R9; £95 for VGC, ++ for EC; Mk I steel-mounted leather scabbard (illustrated).

**222** Pattern 1888 Mk I Bayonet, 2nd type: R3; NRV; with Mk I scabbard about £35; with Mk II scabbard (illustrated) at least £100.

**223** Pattern 1888 Mk II Bayonet: R3/4; NRV; with most common Mk I scabbard about £45; with P 1903 Mk I scabbard (illustrated) about £75.

**224** Pattern 1888 Mk III Bayonet: R6; little RV; VGC with Mk I scabbard £95. Fakes have been encountered made by replacing the brass rivets of earlier versions with screw-bolts.

**225** Pattern 1903 Bayonet: R4; little RV; often with P 1888 Mk I scabbard, about £60; with P 1903 Mk II* scabbard (illustrated) and VGC about £95. All scabbard variations for the P 1888 and P 1903 bayonets are much in demand. Interesting regimental markings and exceptional condition will increase prices above the average.

**226** Pattern 1895 Socket Bayonet: R3/4; NRV; VGC+ with scabbard £75.

**227** Commercial Bayonet, still unidentified: R8; RV; VGC with steel scabbard £400. Well-made fakes made from P 1888 hilts and P 1907 blades with 16.5mm muzzle rings. The genuine bayonet has a smaller 14.5mm ring.

**228** Pattern 1907 Bayonet: R5; with swept forward quillon; VGC-EC £100-125; add £25-30 for Mk I scabbard (illustrated). £200 if made at Lithgow in Australia, £300 if from the Rifle Factory Ishapore in India.

**229** Pattern 1907 Bayonet: R2; NRV; in production for fifty years. Prices vary for interesting regimental markings and manufacturers. Common makers: Wilkinson,

Enfield and Sanderson; less common: Chapman, Lithgow and Isapore; rarer: Mole, Vickers and Remington. VGC £25-40. Add £30 for rare British or Australian double ribbed scabbards.

**230** Pattern 1913 Bayonet: R2; NRV; VGC by Remington about £30, by Winchester about £35, and by Vickers about £125.

**231** No. 4 Mk I Spike Bayonet: R3; NRV; £65. Beware of poor fakes made by machining grooves into a Mk II bayonet. Look out for Mk II markings and badly shaped points.

**232** No. 4 Mk II Spike Bayonet: R1; NRV; £5; add about £3 for Mk II scabbard (illustrated), and about £15 for American-made bayonet with Victory Plastics scabbard.

**233** No. 4 Mk II* Spike Bayonet: R1; NRV; about £5.

**234** No. 4 Mk III Spike Bayonet: R1; NRV; slightly rarer than 233; about £10 with Mk I scabbard, but £15 with plastic Mk III scabbard (illustrated).

**235** Sten SMG Bayonet: R8; £200+, now reproduced in India, no value.

**236** No. 5 Mk I Bayonet: R2; NRV; VGC+ about £60; genuine first patterns with one screw securing the grips about £350, but beware as they are easily faked.

**237** No. 7 Bayonet: R1/2; NRV; VGC+ about £40; slightly more for black grips.

**238** EM2 Bayonet: R9; experimental; £350+. Some fakes have been made but genuine examples have heavier and differently constructed pommels to the No. 7 bayonet.

**239** No. 9 Bayonet: R1; NRV; as little as £20.

**240** L1A3 Bayonet: R3; NRV; VGC+ about £25; L1A1 £100 and L1A4 £30.

### United States of America

**241** Model 1873 Socket Bayonet: R4/5; several belt loop variations; £75.

**242** Model 1873 Cadet Bayonet: R5; £75.

**243** Model 1873 Trowel Bayonet: R4; without scabbard about £200, with scabbard £500.

**244** Model 1892 Krag Bayonet: R4; about £100.

**245** Model 1905 Springfield Bayonet: R4; from £85 to £150 depending on scabbard, early leather examples most desirable.

**246** Model 1917 Enfield Bayonet: R3; NRV; US markings (many sent to Britain as Lend-Lease Arms); about £25.

**247** M1 Bayonet: R2; NRV; several variations; all about £35.

**248** Johnson Bayonet: R4; NRV; £95+.

**249** M4 Knife Bayonet: R3/4; NRV; about £65.

**250** M5 Knife Bayonet: R3; NRV; about £40.

**251** M6 Knife Bayonet: R3; NRV; about £60.

**252** M7 Knife Bayonet: R3; NRV; about £25, with Colt trademark £40+, made in Belgium by FN about £75.

### USSR

**253** Model 1891 Socket Bayonet: R2/3; NRV; about £20; £75+ for the rarer M 1891/30 with foresight guard on the socket.

**254** Model 1915 Winchester Bayonet: R4/5; made in USA; £90+.

**255** Model 1940 Tokarev Bayonet: R8; RV; £100. Rarer M 1938 with 2in longer blade about £300+.

**256** Model 1944 Folding Bayonet: R5; £25.

**257** AK47 Bayonet: R1/2; NRV; £20. East German version with black grips most common.

**258** AKM Bayonet: R1/2; NRV; £25 for a perfect example complete with leather strap, several variations from the Soviet Union available.

### Notes:

1 The highest figure given would be for an example with matching serial numbers on both hilt and scabbard.

2 Add 10% for matching unit markings on hilt and scabbard.

3 Add 20% for any of the rarer steel scabbards and for Saxon or Bavarian markings.

**ARGENTINA: 1.** Model 1891 Bayonet. **AUSTRALIA: 2.** Pattern 1944 Owen SMG Bayonet. **3.** Pattern 1944 Machete Bayonet Mk I. **4.** Pattern 1944 Machete Bayonet Mk II.

**AUSTRIA: 5.** Model 1867 Sabre Bayonet with staghorn grips. **6.** Model 1867 Bayonet. **7.** Model 1870 Bayonet. **8.** Model 1870 NCO's Bayonet.

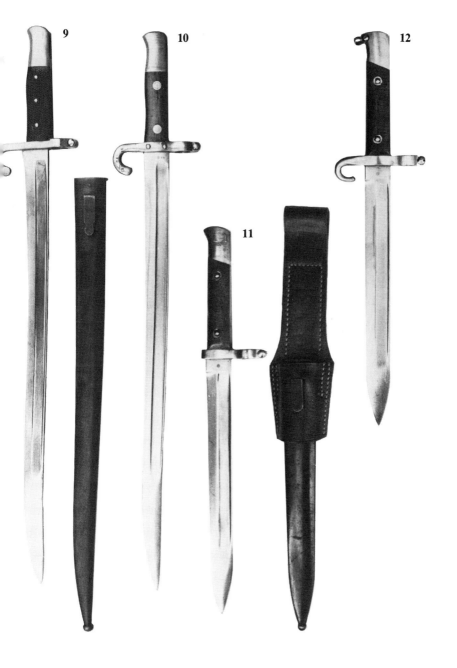

**AUSTRIA: 9.** Model 1873 Bayonet. **10.** Model 1873 Bayonet with wood grips. **11.** Model 1888 Knife Bayonet. **12.** Model 1888 NCO's Knife Bayonet.

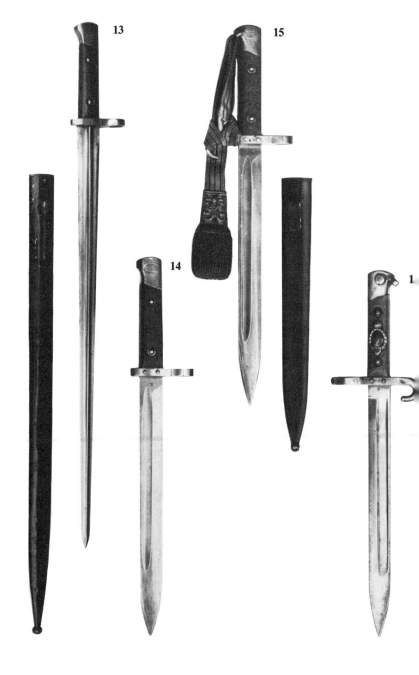

**AUSTRIA: 13.** Model 1895 Gendarmerie Bayonet. **14.** Model 1895 Knife Bayonet. **15.** Model 1895 NCO's Knife Bayonet. **16.** Model 1895 Carbine NCO's Knife Bayonet with enamel regimental badge.

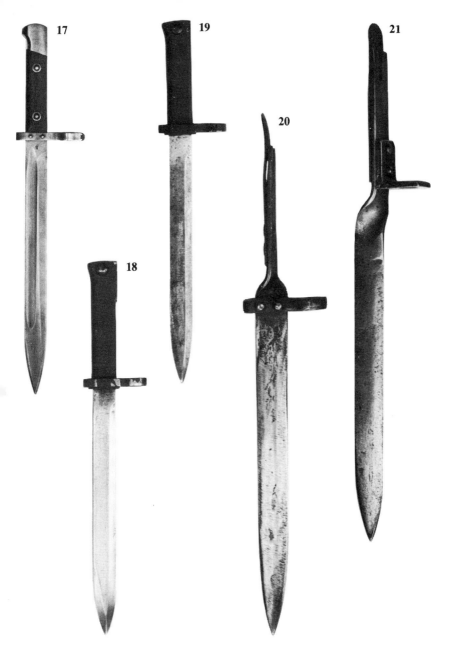

**AUSTRIA: 17.** Model 1895 Carbine Knife Bayonet. **18.** Model 1888 Ersatz Bayonet. **19.** Model 1895 Ersatz Bayonet. **20.** Ersatz Bayonet. **21.** Ersatz Bayonet.

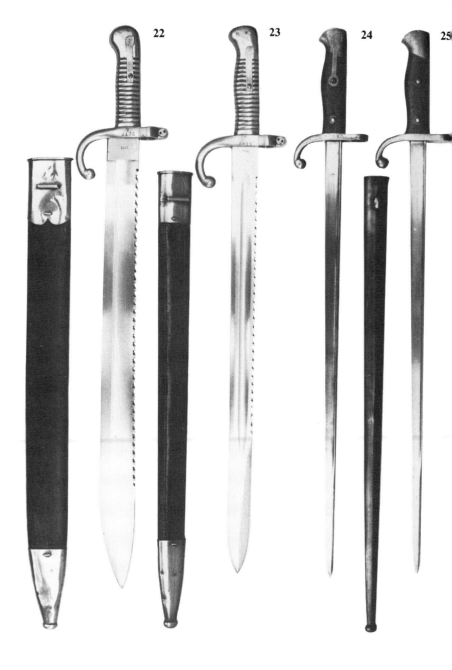

**BELGIUM: 22.** Model 1868 Pioneer Bayonet. **23.** Model 1888 Pioneer Bayonet. **24.** Model 1882 Epée Bayonet. **25.** Model 1882 Bandsman's Bayonet.

**BELGIUM: 26.** Model 1889 Sword Bayonet. **27.** Model 1889 Civil Guard Bayonet. **28.** Model 1889 Infantry Bayonet. **29.** Model 1889 Bayonet made in the USA by Hopkins and Allen.

**BELGIUM: 30.** Model 1916 Epée Bayonet. **31.** Model 1916 Gendarmerie Bayonet. **32.** Model 1924 Epée Bayonet. **CANADA: 33.** Model 1893 Bayonet. **34.** Ross Bayonet Mk I.

**CANADA: 35.** Ross Bayonet Mk II. **36.** C1 Bayonet. **CHINA: 37.** German Model 1871 Bayonet exported to China. **38.** Belgian-made Bayonet, c.1920.

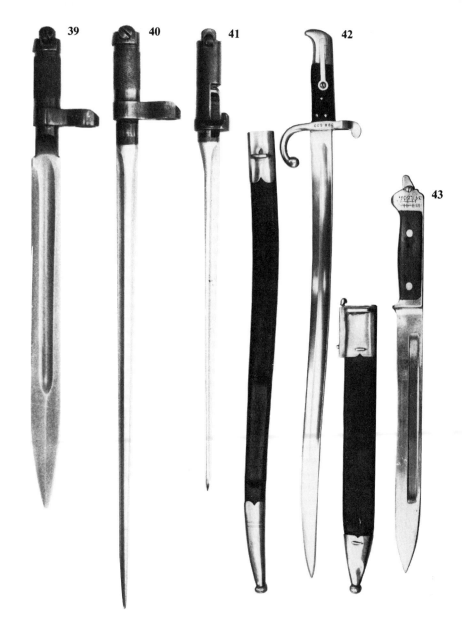

**CHINA: 39.** Type 53 (SKS) Folding Bayonet. **40.** Type 53 (SKS) Folding Bayonet. **41.** Type 56 (AK) Folding Bayonet. **DENMARK: 42.** Model 1867 Sabre Bayonet. **43.** Model 1889 Knife Bayonet with wooden grips.

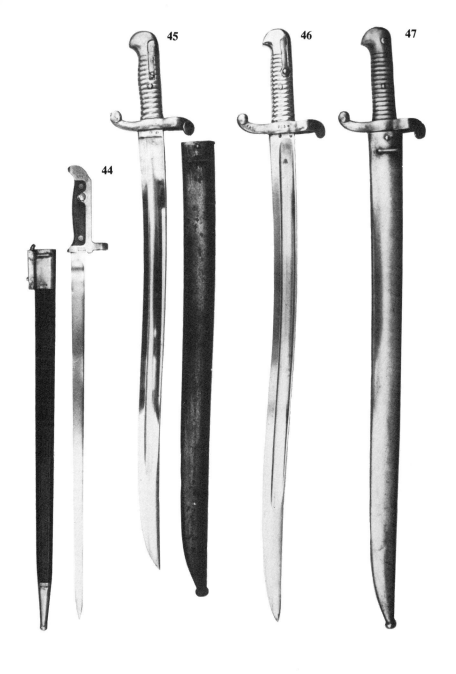

**DENMARK: 44.** Model 1915 Bayonet. **FRANCE: 45.** Model 1840 Sabre Bayonet. **46.** Model 1842 Sabre Bayonet. **47.** Model 1842/59 Sabre Bayonet.

**FRANCE: 48.** Model 1866 Sabre Bayonet. **49.** Model 1866 Socket Bayonet. **50.** Model 1874 Epée Bayonet. **51.** Model 1878 Kropatschek Bayonet.

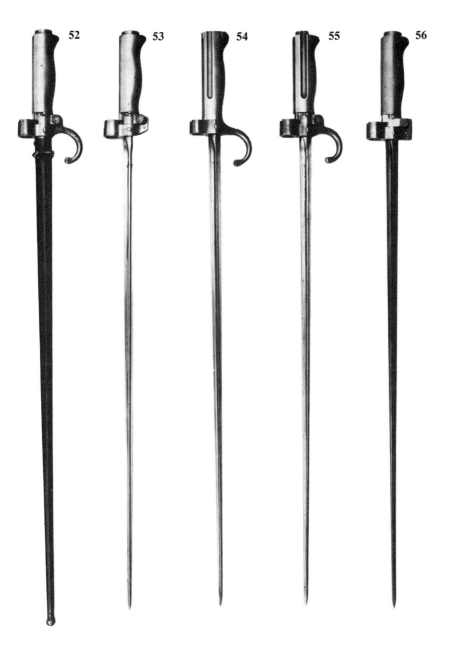

**FRANCE: 52.** Model 1886 Epée Bayonet. **53.** Model 1886/15 Epée Bayonet. **54.** Model 1890 Gendarmerie Bayonet. **55.** Model 1895 Daudeteau Bayonet. **56.** Model 1886/93/16 Bayonet with brass hilt.

**FRANCE: 57.** Model 1886/93/16 Bayonet with blued steel hilt. **58.** Model
1886/93/16/35 Bayonet. **59.** Model 1892 Bayonet. **60.** Model 1892/15
Bayonet. **61.** Model 1892 Bayonet.

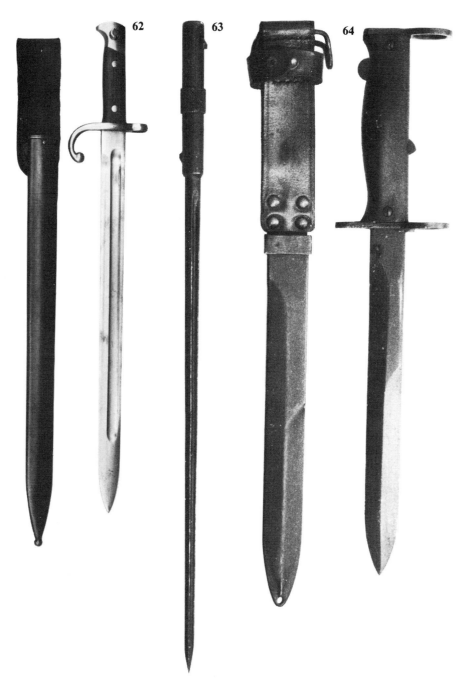

**FRANCE: 62.** Model 1914 Bayonet. **63.** Model 1936 MAS Rod Bayonet.
**64.** Model 1949/56 MAS Knife Bayonet.

**GERMANY: 65.** Prussian Model 1860 Fusilier Bayonet. **66.** Prussian Model 1865 Jaeger Bayonet. **67.** Prussian Model 1865 Pioneer Bayonet.

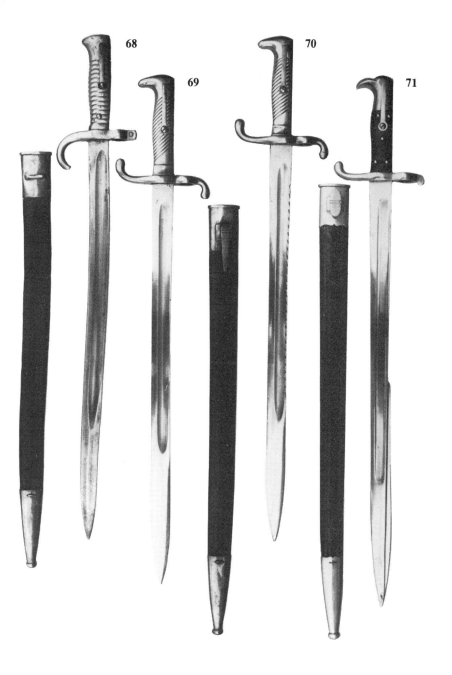

**GERMANY: 68.** Bavarian Model 1869 Bayonet. **69.** Prussian Model 1871 Infantry Bayonet. **70.** Prussian Model 1871 Infantry NCO's Bayonet. **71.** Prussian Model 1871 Jaeger Bayonet.

**GERMANY: 72.** Bavarian Model 1871 Pioneer Bayonet. **73.** Wurttemberg Model 1871 Pioneer Bayonet. **74.** Prussian Model 1871 Walking Out Bayonet. **75.** Prussian Model 1871 NCO's Walking Out Bayonet.

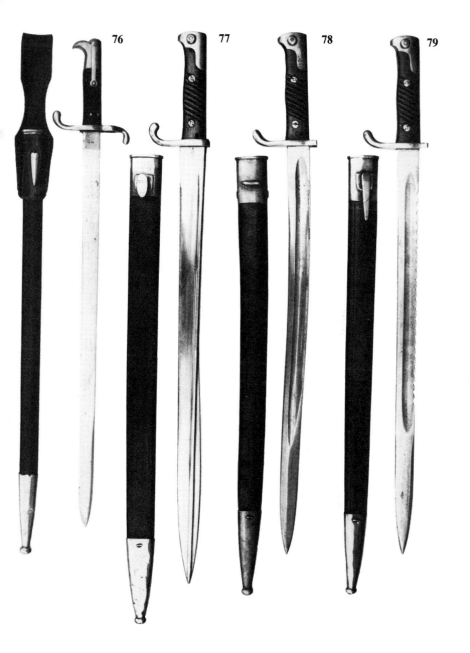

**GERMANY: 76.** Prussian Model 1871 Jaeger Walking Out Bayonet. **77.** Model 1860/98 Bayonet. **78.** Model 1869/98 Bayonet. **79.** Model 1869/98 Bayonet.

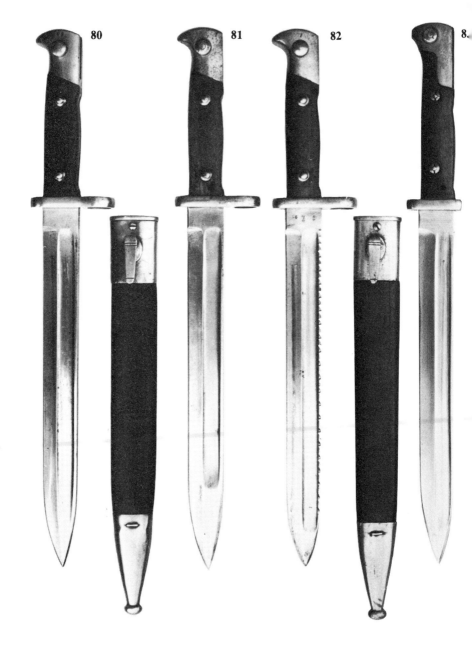

**GERMANY: 80.** Model 1871/84 Knife Bayonet. **81.** Model 1871/84 Knife Bayonet. **82.** Model 1871/84 NCO's Knife Bayonet. **83.** Model 1884/98 Knife Bayonet.

**GERMANY: 84.** Short Model 1898 Knife Bayonet (KS 98). **85.** Short Model 1898 Knife Bayonet (KS 98). **86.** Model 1898 Bayonet, 1st pattern with one-piece wood grip. **87.** Model 1898 NCO's Bayonet, 1st pattern. **88.** Model 1898 Bayonet, 2nd pattern with two-piece grips.

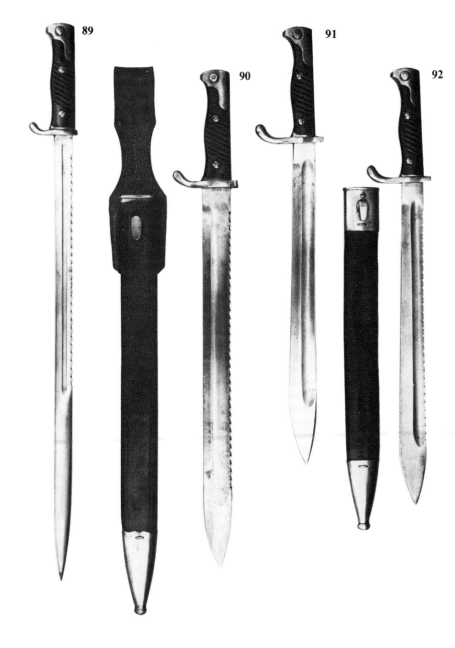

GERMANY: **89.** Model 1898 NCO's Bayonet, 2nd pattern. **90.** Model 1898/02 Bayonet. **91.** Model 1898/05 Bayonet, 1st pattern. **92.** Model 1898/05 Saw-Backed Bayonet, 1st pattern.

**GERMANY: 93.** Model 1898/05 Bayonet, 2nd pattern. **94.** Model 1898/05 Saw-Backed Bayonet, 2nd pattern. **95.** Model 1898/05 Bayonet with saw-back removed. **96.** Model 1914 Bayonet. **97.** Model 1914 Bayonet.

**GERMANY: 98.** Model 1914 Saw-Backed Bayonet. **99.** Bavarian Model 1914 Bayonet. **100.** Bavarian Model 1914 Saw-Backed Bayonet. **101.** Ersatz Combination Knife Bayonet.

**GERMANY: 102.** Ersatz Combination Knife Bayonet. **103.** Ersatz Bayonet. **104.** Ersatz Bayonet. **105.** Ersatz Bayonet. **106.** Ersatz Bayonet.

**GERMANY: 107.** Ersatz Bayonet. **108.** Ersatz Bayonet. **109.** Ersatz Bayonet. **110.** Ersatz Bayonet.

**GERMANY: 111.** Ersatz Bayonet. **112.** Ersatz Bayonet. **113.** Ersatz
Bayonet. **114.** Ersatz Bayonet.

**GERMANY: 115.** Ersatz Bayonet. **116.** Ersatz Bayonet. **117.** Ersatz Bayonet. **118.** Ersatz Bayonet.

**GERMANY: 119.** Ersatz Bayonet. **120.** Ersatz Bayonet. **121.** Ersatz
Bayonet. **122.** Ersatz Bayonet.

**GERMANY: 123.** Ersatz Bayonet. **124.** Ersatz Bayonet. **125.** Ersatz Bayonet. **126.** Model 1884/98 Knife Bayonet, 1915–18 production.

**GERMANY: 127.** Model 1884/98 Saw-Backed Knife Bayonet, 1915–18.
**128.** Model 1884/98 Knife Bayonet, 3rd Reich. **129.** Model 1884/98 Knife
Bayonet, 3rd Reich. **130.** Czech Model 1924 Bayonet, 3rd Reich.

**GREECE: 131.** Model 1874 Bayonet; identical to the French M 1874 but inscribed Waffenfabrik Steyr and dated. **132.** Model 1874/03 Bayonet; muzzle ring replaced by one to fit the Model 1903 rifle. **133.** Model 1874/03 Bayonet. **134.** Model 1903 Bayonet.

**GREECE: 135.** Model 1903 Bayonet. **136.** Model 1903 Knife Bayonet.
**HOLLAND: 137.** Model 1873 Beaumont Sabre Bayonet. **138.** Model 1895
Sword Bayonet.

**HOLLAND: 139.** Model 1895 Bayonet. **140.** Model 1895 Marine Bayonet.
**141.** Model 1895 Cavalry Bayonet. **142.** AR10 Knife Bayonet.

**INDIA: 143.** India Pattern Mk I**. **144.** India Pattern Mk II*. **145.** India Pattern Mk II. **146.** India Pattern Mk III.

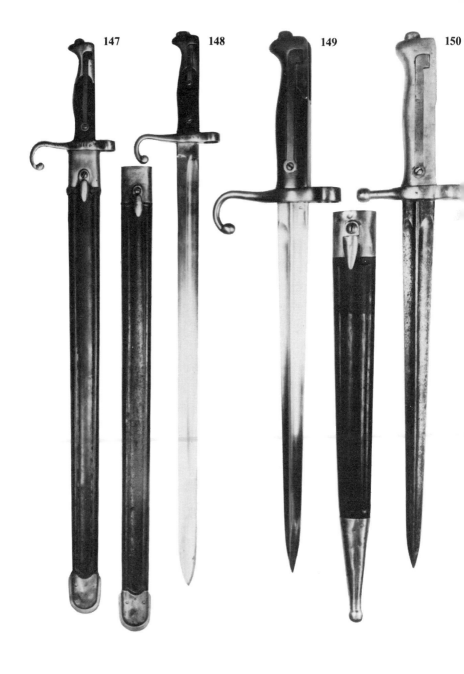

**ITALY: 147.** Model 1870 Sword Bayonet. **148.** Model 1870–87 Sword Bayonet. **149.** Model 1870 T.S. Bayonet. **150.** Model 1870 T.S. Bayonet.

**ITALY: 151.** Model 1870 Shortened Bayonet. **152.** Model 1870/15 Knife Bayonet. **153.** Model 1891 Bayonet.

ITALY: **154.** Model 1891 Bayonet. **155.** Model 1891 T.S. Bayonet. **156.** Model 1938 Folding Bayonet. **157.** Model 1938 Beretta Folding Bayonet.

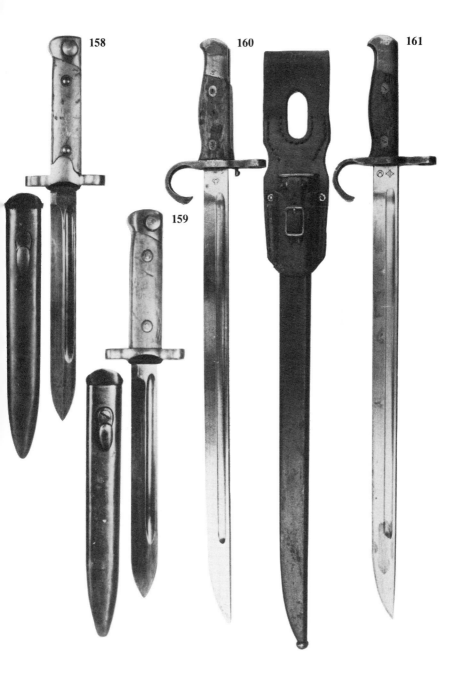

**ITALY: 158.** Model 1938 Modified Bayonet. **159.** Model 1938 Bayonet.
**JAPAN: 160.** Model 1897 Marine Bayonet. **161.** Model 1897 Bayonet.

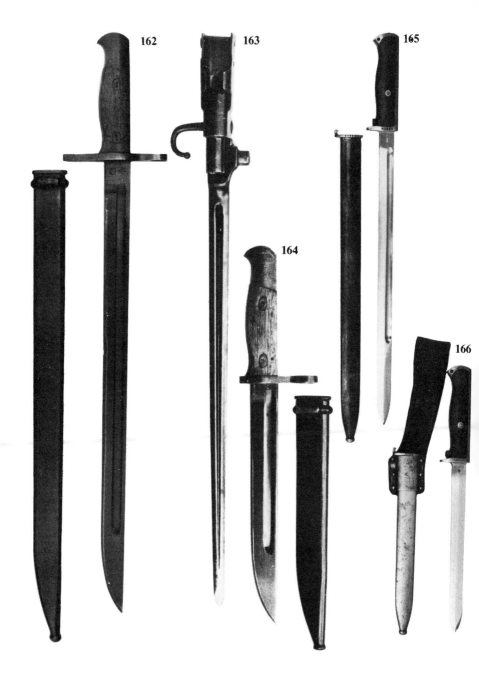

**JAPAN: 162.** Model 1897 Bayonet. **163.** Model 1911 Folding Bayonet.
**164.** Model 1940 SMG Knife Bayonet. **NORWAY: 165.** Model 1894
Bayonet. **166.** Model 1894 Knife Bayonet.

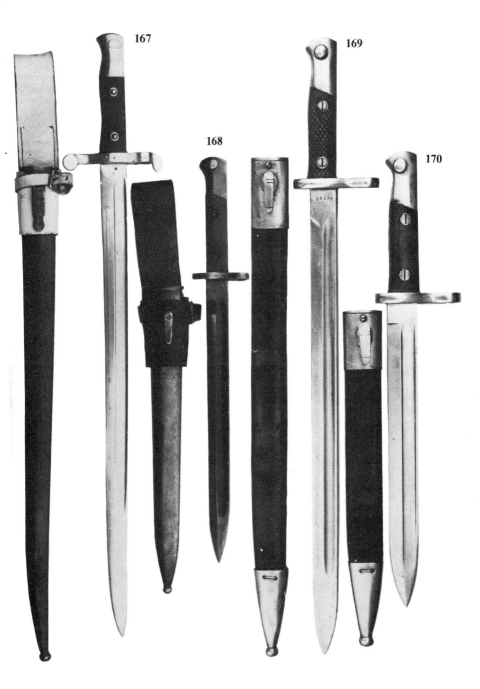

**PORTUGAL: 167.** Model 1886 Sword Bayonet. **168.** Model 1904 Bayonet. **SPAIN: 169.** Model 1893 Artillery Bayonet. **170.** Model 1893 Knife Bayonet.

**SPAIN: 171.** Model 1943 Knife Bayonet. **172.** Model 1943 Knife Bayonet.
**173.** Model 1941 Bolo Bayonet. **174.** Model 1958 Cetme Bayonet.

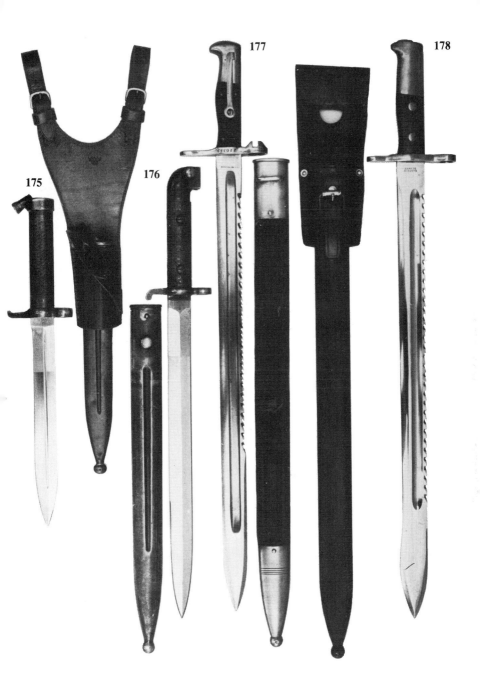

**SWEDEN: 175.** Model 1896 Knife Bayonet. **176.** Model 1914 Bayonet.
**SWITZERLAND: 177.** Model 1878 Vetterli Engineers Bayonet. **178.**
Model 1914 Schmidt-Rubin Engineers Bayonet.

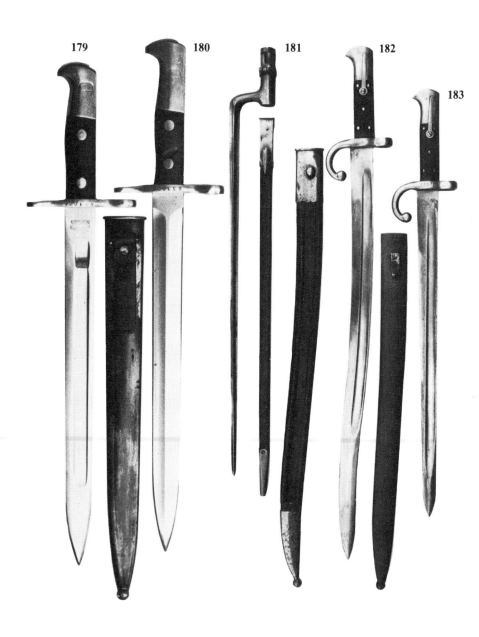

**SWITZERLAND: 179.** Model 1889 Bayonet. **180.** Model 1918 Bayonet. **TURKEY: 181.** Model 1874 Socket Bayonet. **182.** Model 1874 Sword Bayonet. **183.** Model 1874 Shortened Bayonet.

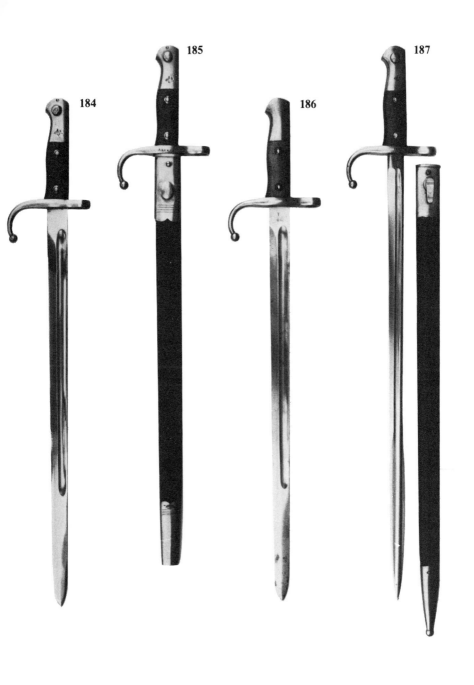

**TURKEY: 184.** Model 1887 Bayonet. **185.** Model 1890 Bayonet. **186.** Model 1890 Band Bayonet. **187.** Model 1903 Bayonet.

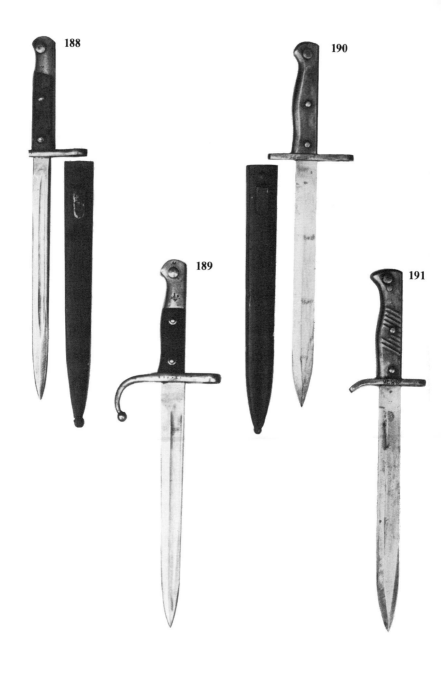

**TURKEY: 188.** Model 1903 Knife Bayonet. **189.** Model 1890 Shortened Bayonet. **190.** Ersatz Bayonet. **191.** Ersatz Bayonet.

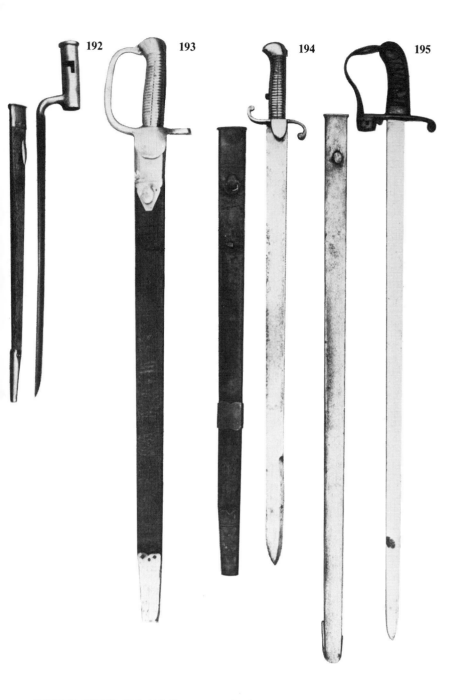

**UNITED KINGDOM: 192.** Brown Bess Socket Bayonet. **193.** Baker Sword Bayonet, 2nd pattern. **194.** Baker Volunteer Sword Bayonet. **195.** Volunteer Sword Bayonet.

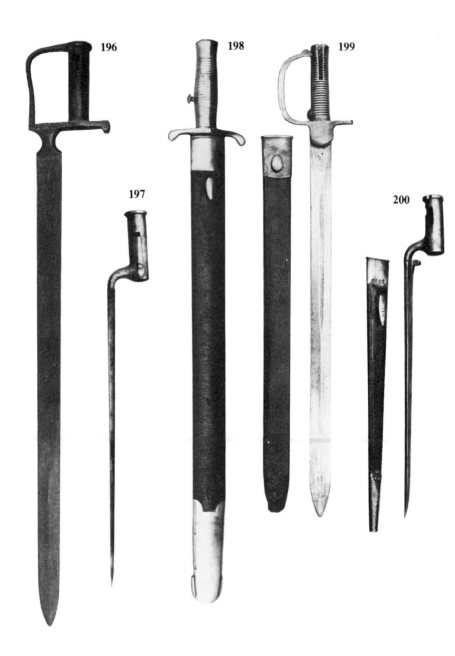

**UNITED KINGDOM: 196.** Volunteer Sword Socket Bayonet. **197.** New Land Pattern Socket Bayonet. **198.** Pattern 1837 Brunswick Sword Bayonet. **199.** Constabulary Brunswick Sword Bayonet. **200.** Pattern 1840 Constabulary Socket Bayonet.

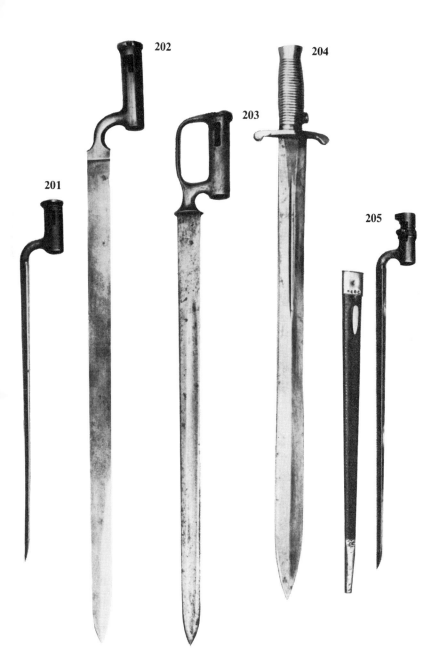

**UNITED KINGDOM: 201.** Pattern 1842 Socket Bayonet. **202.** Pattern 1843 Sappers & Miners Sword Socket Bayonet. **203.** East India Company Sword Socket Bayonet. **204.** Pattern 1847 Brunswick Sword Bayonet. **205.** Pattern 1853 Socket Bayonet.

**UNITED KINGDOM: 206.** Pattern 1853 Artillery Sword Bayonet. **207.**
Pattern 1855 Lancaster Sword Bayonet. **208.** Volunteer Sword Bayonet.
**209.** Pattern 1856 Sword Bayonet.

**UNITED KINGDOM: 210.** Pattern 1859 Naval Cutlass Bayonet. **211.** Volunteer Sword Bayonet. **212.** Jacobs Sword Bayonet. **213.** Pattern 1871 Elcho Bayonet.

**UNITED KINGDOM: 214.** Pattern 1871 Naval Cutlass Bayonet. **215.** Pattern 1875 Artillery Bayonet. **216.** Pattern 1876 Socket Bayonet. **217.** Pattern 1879 Artillery Sword Bayonet.

**UNITED KINGDOM: 218.** Pattern 1887 Mk I Sword Bayonet. **219.**
Pattern 1887 Mk III Sword Bayonet. **220.** Pattern 1887 Mk IV Sword
Bayonet. **221.** Pattern 1888 Mk I Bayonet with Mk I steel-mounted leather
scabbard.

**UNITED KINGDOM: 222.** Pattern 1888 Mk I Bayonet, 2nd type, with Mk II scabbard. **223.** Pattern 1888 Mk II Bayonet with P 1903 Mk I scabbard. **224.** Pattern 1888 Mk III Bayonet. **225.** Pattern 1903 Bayonet with P 1903 Mk II* scabbard.

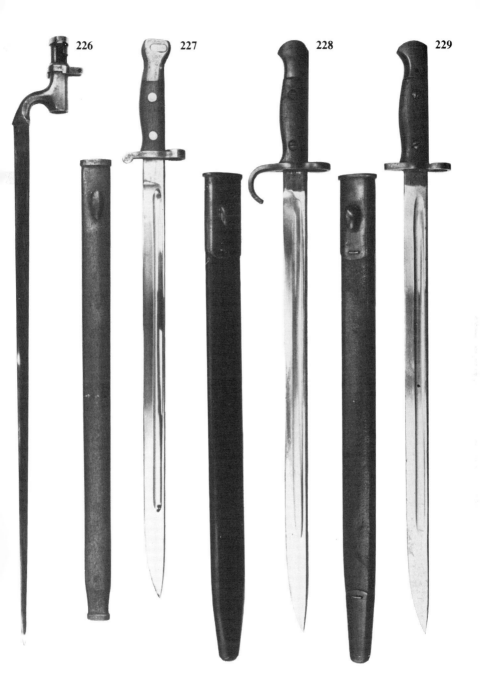

**UNITED KINGDOM: 226.** Pattern 1895 Socket Bayonet. **227.** Commercial Bayonet, possibly Ulster Volunteer Force. **228.** Pattern 1907 Bayonet with Mk I scabbard. **229.** Pattern 1907 Bayonet.

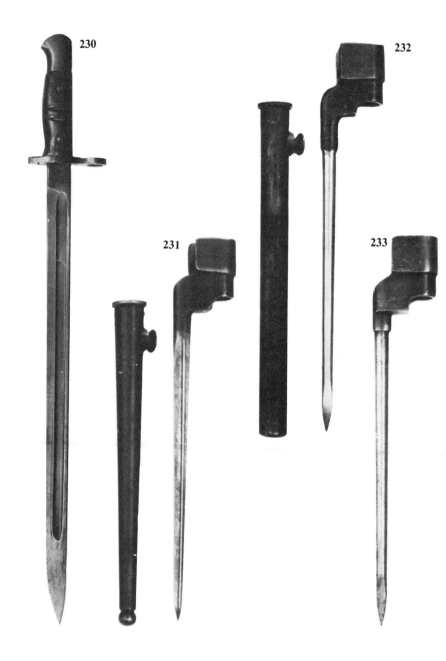

**UNITED KINGDOM: 230.** Pattern 1913 Bayonet. **231.** No. 4 Mk I Spike Bayonet. **232.** No. 4 Mk II Spike Bayonet with Mk II scabbard. **233.** No. 4 Mk II* Spike Bayonet.

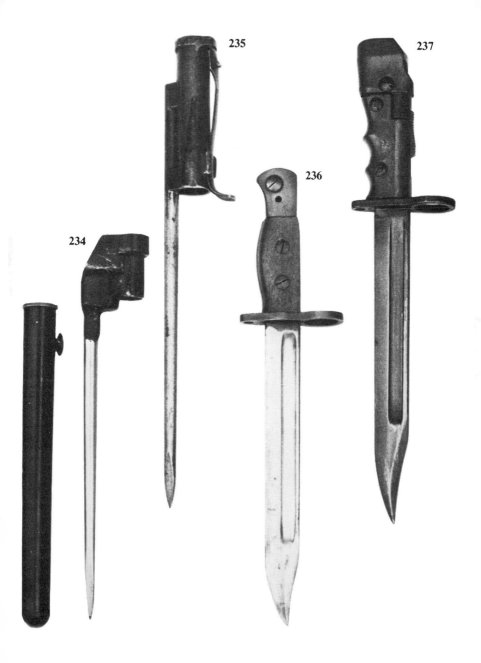

**UNITED KINGDOM: 234.** No. 4 Mk III Spike Bayonet with plastic Mk III scabbard. **235.** Sten SMG Bayonet. **236.** No. 5 Mk I Bayonet. **237.** No. 7 Bayonet.

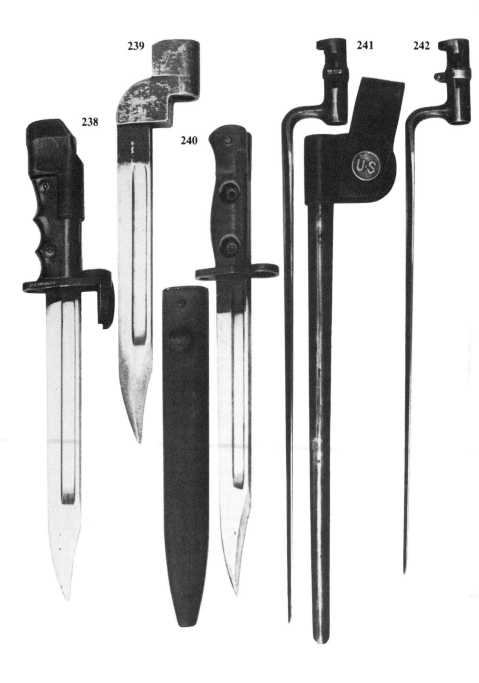

**UNITED KINGDOM: 238.** EM2 Bayonet. **239.** No. 9 Bayonet. **240.** L1A3 Bayonet. **UNITED STATES OF AMERICA: 241.** Model 1873 Socket Bayonet. **242.** Model 1873 Cadet Bayonet.

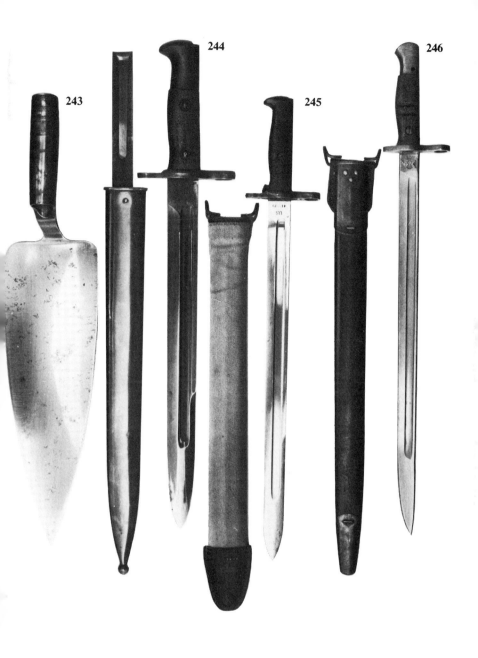

**UNITED STATES OF AMERICA: 243.** Model 1873 Trowel Bayonet. **244.** Model 1892 Krag Bayonet. **245.** Model 1905 Springfield Bayonet. **246.** Model 1917 Enfield Bayonet.

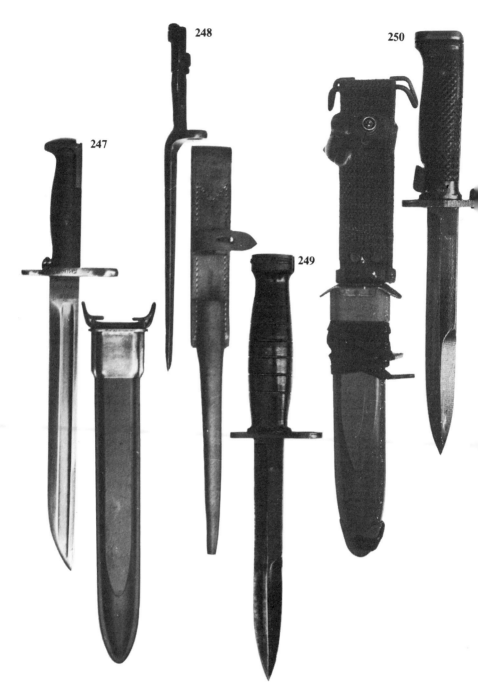

**UNITED STATES OF AMERICA: 247.** M1 Bayonet. **248.** Johnson Bayonet. **249.** M4 Knife Bayonet. **250.** M5 Knife Bayonet.

**UNITED STATES OF AMERICA: 251.** M6 Knife Bayonet. **252.** M7 Knife Bayonet. **USSR: 253.** Model 1891 Socket Bayonet. **254.** Model 1915 Winchester Bayonet.

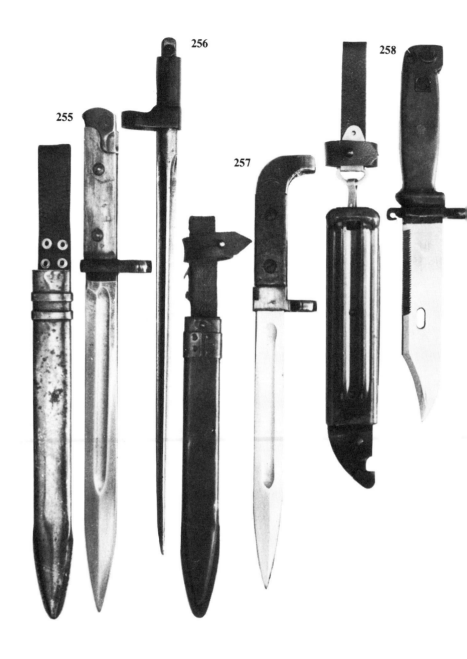

**USSR: 255.** Model 1940 Tokarev Bayonet. **256.** Model 1944 Folding Bayonet. **257.** AK47 Bayonet. **258** AKM Bayonet.